Camping

New Zea

GW00672141

contents

Introduction

North Island camping sites

South Island car

Matai Bay, Northland. Photo Destination Northland

Kia Ora

Like many New Zealanders, my childhood is full of fond memories of kiwi camping and beautiful beachside summers. The first sign of the treats to come was my father packing our humble car with tents and camping paraphernalia. Sagging on its suspension and loaded to the roof, the car would then struggle to the chosen destination making frequent stops either to refresh the children in the back seat with ice creams, or to relieve occasional bouts of motion sickness.

The resulting holidays created a feast of fond memories; the warmth of sun on skin, cool refreshing waters, my first attempts at swimming, new friendships, childhood romances, rafting on inner tubes, my first fish, boating, water-skiing, sailing, eating from the campfire, and the eerie nocturnal noises associated with sleeping under canvas.

I didn't appreciate it then, but I now realize how fortunate I was. Not only is New Zealand one of the most beautiful countries in the world, it is one of the few countries where such natural treats are so accessible to so many.

Long before the *Lord of the Rings* movie trilogy redefined New Zealand's scenic wonders, a 1936 National Geographic article exclaimed: "here in an area approximately the size of Colorado are grouped the snow-mantled peaks of a Switzerland, geysers of a Yellowstone, volcanic cones of Java and Japan, and the lakes of Italy: the mineral springs of Czechoslovakia, the fjords of Norway, sea coasts of Maine and California, and waterfalls higher than Yosemite."

In more recent years as I travelled widely in Australia, Europe, Asia and the Middle East, I increasingly appreciated New Zealand's egalitarian accessibility to relatively 'clean and green' scenery. It is has been my pleasure to be involved in writing and researching this publication so the many happy experiences associated with Kiwi camping can be more easily discovered by others.

However, along with this pleasure I am conscious of a responsibility to preserve the heritage of camping as well as New Zealand's unique natural environment. So while this guide will allow you to find your own magical memories of Kiwi camping in our beautiful country, I hope you will also keep in mind some of the responsibilities that campers must follow in order to ensure our cherished and fragile environment is available to future generations to enjoy as we have.

My heartfelt thanks to Donna who accompanied me on these journeys and who helped so ably with the research. Thanks also to Henry, Ed, Gavin, Natalie, Ross and the rest of the team at Hema Maps for their support, skills and vision.

Safe travelling

Peter Mitchell

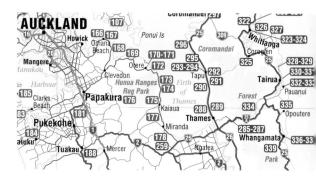

How to use this book

Simply view the map section for the area(s) that you wish to travel to, and find the relevant numbers for the area that interests you. Then find the number in the listing of motorhome parks, campsites and rest areas for information about the site you have chosen. Once you have selected an appropriate camp you can use the address details with a Hema Atlas product, or the GPS information, to locate the site.

Campsites

All of the campsites detailed in this guide are grouped into the following broad categories:

Serviced Campsite

These sites have regular (usually daily) servicing of toilets and showers, and they often also have a variety of other services that can make your camping a delight. Such sites are normally commercial and payment is required.

Motorhome Park/Caravan Park

These sites offer a similar level of facilities to a serviced campsite, but are also suitable for campervans.

Motorhome Park/Caravan Park with dump station

These sites are motorhome park/caravan parks that also provide dump stations.

Informal Camping

This classification covers a wide variety of Department of Conservation (DoC) or local authority domain camping grounds where servicing is perhaps less regular, and facilities are more limited. Such areas should in no means be regarded as second-rate camping compared to their commercial alternatives; indeed such simple camping is often the very essence of what 'real Kiwi camping' is about. Indeed the scenic location of many casual camping sites means they provide highly memorable camping.

Roadside Rest Area

There are roadside rest areas (including short term parking and picnic areas) everywhere in New Zealand; and they range from scruffy patches of gravel used by road maintenance crews to pretty spots with seating, tables and shade for weary travellers to rest. It is impossible to mark every roadside gravel patch, so to rate a mention in this guide, acceptable rest areas need at least one of the following: picnic table, barbecue or fireplace, toilet, shade or shelter, or a worthwhile view.

Hawke's Bay vines. Photo Hawke's Bay Tourism.

Site information

The details for the sites will include the following symbols and information:

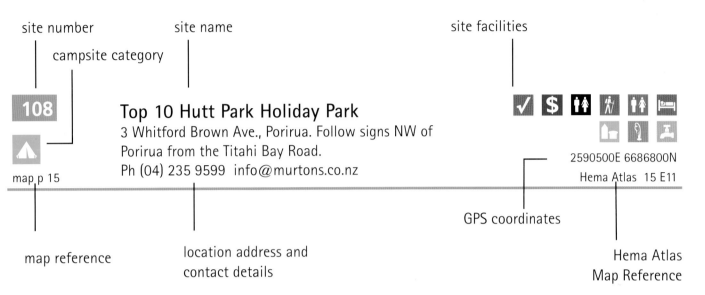

site number

campsite category

site name

site facilities

108

Top 10 Hutt Park Holiday Park
3 Whitford Brown Ave., Porirua. Follow signs NW of
Porirua from the Titahi Bay Road.
Ph (04) 235 9599 info@murtons.co.nz

2590500E 6686800N
Hema Atlas 15 E11

map p 15

GPS coordinates

map reference

location address and
contact details

Hema Atlas
Map Reference

 **Site number**

This arbitrary number has been allocated to enable you to find each site on the location map, and conversely to find a site's details from the location map. To order these sites New Zealand's two islands have been divided into regions, with touring routes followed within each district.

Campsite category

Each campsite has been classified as either a serviced campsite, motorhome park/caravan park, motorhome park/caravan park with dump station, informal camping or roadside rest area (see above). These symbols appear on Hema Maps' range of atlas products (see Hema Atlas Map Reference for more information).

Map 12 C3 | **Map reference**

This reference relates to the location maps in the front of this book. These basic maps have been supplied to provide an easy way to find the numbers for the sites in the areas you wish to visit. Or, if you are looking at a site's details, you can use the reference to find the relevant location map for a quick idea of where the campsite is situated.

Name & address details

This includes only the key contact details such as standard phone and email addresses. Free-phone reservation numbers, prefixed by 0800 or 0508, are included where this service is available. Road directions to help you find the site are also included where relevant.

Notes

This includes further handy information, for example about bookings and opening times, as well as comments from the author about the site.

Site Facilities

✓ **Author recommended**

These are the camps that particularly appealed to the author. It may have been the friendly welcome, great location or little 'service' extras. Some are casual camps with a possible Qualmark rating of only one or two stars, whilst others may be more expensive 'upmarket' four or five star rated. Whilst the author's personal taste may not be your 'cup of tea', he believes these camps usually offer something a little extra, and are worth checking out.

$ **Fees apply**

Payment will be required for camping at these sites, but rates aren't included as these are subject to constant change. Use the contact details of the camp to check the current rates. (See also the comments on 'Free Camping' page 10.)

Toilets

Toilet usage is usually free in New Zealand, however quality and cleanliness levels can fluctuate widely (especially in more remote areas).

Water

Water is provided at these sites, and it is usually of a standard suitable for drinking. (At some DoC camps only stream water is provided.) The author accepts no liability or responsibility for determining water quality, but simply points out that standards in New Zealand are usually high. If you are in doubt about water quality ask the locals, or take appropriate steps to sterilize the water. (See the later section on Drinking Water for more information.)

Showers

Showers (usually hot) are provided here, although no judgment is made as to the quality. In some cases extra payment (usually 20c or 50c) is needed to feed slot machines and shower times may be limited to five to eight minutes. In general, campsites charging extra for showers are not widespread and are relatively rare in the South Island.

Laundry

This indicates that clothes washing facilities are provided. Most serviced camps supply coin-operated washing facilities, usually requiring $2 coins.

Kitchen facilities

Most camps with kitchen facilities will also provide hotplates, ovens, microwaves, refrigerators, freezers, toasters and kettles (or alternative means for boiling water). Some go further and provide utensils and cleaning materials. Barbecues are becoming quite common at most serviced camps, although some may require a coin to operate.

Electricity

This indicates that powered sites are available for campervans, RVs, caravans or even for campers in tents to use.

Cabins

Cabins are available at these sites, but the author makes no comment on the quality. Holiday parks and camping grounds often offer small cabins for the use of campers. Rates are usually more expensive than for tent camping, but they are much cheaper than hotel or motel rates. Linen (sheets and towels) are not normally provided in such cabins as you are expected to use your own sleeping gear. However, if needed, linen is usually available for an extra charge.

Shop

Usually such campsite shops are well equipped to supply any essentials that you may have forgotten. However, standards vary considerably and you are advised to be as self-contained as possible.

Boat launch

This indicates that boat launching facilities are available, either within the camp or nearby.

Swimming pool

A swimming pool is available to campers at this site.

Thermal pool

A mineral or thermal pool is available to campers at this site.

Disabled facilities

Some campsites make a special mention of this feature, and we have listed those here. However, the provision of disabled facilities is now

Camping in the River Region

Destination Taranaki

Canterbury region

Christchurch Canterbury Marketing

Near Glenorchy

Destination Queenstown

entrenched in NZ building codes and you can expect all modern serviced camps above two star ratings to have suitable facilities.

Wastewater disposal facilities

Most serviced campsites are now offering suitable facilities to empty your toilet waste and 'grey water'. There may be a charge for using a dump station at some camping grounds, unless you are staying there. (Under no circumstances is it acceptable to dispose of wastewater in rubbish disposal facilities.)

Pets allowed

Although pets are permitted at these sites conditions may apply. In preparing this book the author found the question of pets in camps is subject to much debate. Many serviced motor camps and holiday parks will welcome a well-behaved pet, but in general there is widespread caution surrounding the issue of pets in camps.

There are many campsites that clearly request 'No Pets'. This includes the Department of Conservation national parks, and most regional parks, where dogs and cats can kill native bird populations and nesting birds.

The author strongly recommends that your pet is left behind when you go on a camping holiday unless you have secured permission in advance to bring your pet to your chosen campsites.

Scenic

This indicates that, in the opinion of the author, this site has particular scenic advantages or is close to scenic viewpoints.

Walks

There are some interesting walking opportunities located in the area surrounding this site.

GPS coordinates

GPS technology is becoming more widespread, particularly in rental vehicles, so New Zealand Map Grid Eastings and Northings have been included to assist you in locating your chosen campsite. (Your position can be displayed as either Eastings and Northings or Latitude and Longitude on your GPS unit.)

Please be aware that to provide an accurate GPS reading the receiver must be able to 'see' at least three or four of the satellites and be clear of buildings or thick vegetation. The accuracy of the information listed here could possibly have been effected by these variables. As with any other method of navigation, you should not rely solely on your GPS. See the 'Using a GPS with your atlas' section on the legend panel inside the back cover for more information.

Hema Atlas Map Reference

All of the sites listed in this book are shown in the 2nd edition (2007) of Hema Maps' New Zealand Atlas range – Road Atlas, Touring Atlas and Handy Atlas. Simply use the reference, along with the address details, to find the site on the relevant Hema Atlas page.

Change is certain

Every attempt has been made to ensure that the information supplied is accurate at the time of publication. However the management and ownership of camps constantly changes, and no responsibility is accepted by the author or publisher for any decisions or actions taken on the basis of information contained in this publication.

Updates

Campsite standards and services are always subject to change, and new facilities and services open up as old ones close down. The publisher welcomes

Kapiti Island

Municipal Chambers, Dunedin

Matai Bay

Centre Stage

Tourism Dunedin

Destination Northland

information and suggestions for corrections or feedback. If you find any information has changed or you know of other suitable campsites for inclusion, then please write or email and let us know so we can update the information in subsequent editions. [Hema Maps, PO Box 58924, Greenmount, East Tamaki, Auckland or email sales@hemamaps.co.nz]

The quality of Kiwi camping

The experience of camping is often seen as an opportunity to 'get back to basics'; a chance to strip away the complications of civilization and escape to the 'simple life.' The only problem is that many of us cannot escape without the essentials of life, such as hairdryers, televisions, radios, microwaves, refrigerators, and hot and cold water on tap. It is these 'essentials' that serviced or commercial campsites are often expected to provide. Thus your enjoyment of campsites can be very much driven by your needs.

New Zealand camping grounds are generally of a very high standard. However, standards do vary as owners or managers come and go. What was a good camp a year ago, may no longer be so. Likewise what was once a poor camp can be improved by new and energetic management.

This guide is based on the standards that we found in camps during 2006, and I stress that this view is one moment in time and it is entirely my view. You may well find different conditions, and your needs may well be different from mine. Accordingly I stress that any views on the appeal or quality of the campsites is entirely mine and you are invited to explore and reach your own conclusions.

West Coast scenery, South Island

Tourism West Coast

Qualmark

The Qualmark symbol is a worthy attempt to define the 'quality' of camping and accommodation in New Zealand. While it is an excellent system, its major limitation is that camps are charged an annual fee for a Qualmark assessment and not all camps are willing or able to pay for such a privilege. Thus, many DoC camps as well as those run by regional councils, local bodies and smaller family-run or whanau-managed campsites are not Qualmark assessed. However, this lack of assessment is often no indication of their quality or charm.

It should also be noted that the Qualmark assessment does not take into account the scenic quality of the camp's location. So a beachside DoC or whanau-managed camp might only achieve a one star rating for its facilities of toilets and cold water. However, the scenery and peacefulness of the experience can more than compensate for such a low rating.

The Qualmark system of ratings defines quality as follows:

Rating	Definition
★	**Acceptable** – meets customers' minimum requirements
★★	**Good** – exceeds customers' minimum quality standards
★★★	**Very good** – good to very good quality facilities and services
★★★★	**Excellent** – consistently achieves high quality levels
★★★★★	**Exceptional** – among the best in NZ

In my view the majority of serviced campsites and holiday parks in New Zealand are the equivalent of a two star Qualmark rating or better.

Other associations

In addition to the Qualmark system, there are those serviced camping grounds that form associations with the intention of improving standards, and working together to optimise service, marketing and business opportunities. Key amongst these groups are Top 10 Holiday Parks and Holiday Accommodation Parks of NZ (HAPNZ).

Top 10 Holiday Parks

To be a member of this grouping campsites need to be independently assessed by Qualmark at a standard of four stars or better. In my experience the Top 10 Holiday Parks are managed extremely well, and offer excellent service. The only downside to these excellent camps is that due to their popularity they can get a little crowded, and prices tend to be higher than other more simple options. (See www.topparks.co.nz for more information.)

Holiday Accommodation Parks of NZ (HAPNZ)

This association offers a more diverse range of quality than Top 10. Parks under this scheme are generally the equivalent of good or very good standards – i.e. three star or more. (See www.holidayparks. co.nz for more information.)

NZ Motor Caravan Association

As you travel the roads in New Zealand you will notice many caravans and mobile campers displaying a small red 'wing' logo. These travellers are members of the New Zealand Motor Caravan Association (NZMCA).

Membership of NZMCA is strongly recommended for those who anticipate doing a lot of camping using caravans, campervans and buses. The NZMCA offers a wide range of discounts and special offers. In addition, members of the NZMCA offer 'Park over Properties' (POPs) for the exclusive use of fellow members. These overnight camping areas are spread throughout New Zealand, but they are not depicted in this book as they are intended for the exclusive use of NZMCA members. If you want to find out more about POPs or how to utilize them you must be a member of NZMCA. (For more information visit the website www.nzmca.org.nz or ph (09) 298 5466.)

'Free camping'

It all seems so simple, just roll up to a quiet campsite, pitch your tent, sit around the evening campfire telling yarns – and the next day, move on and find another idyllic location. The reality is that such 'free camping' is seldom so free. You might ask: who mows the grass and keeps the area free of rubbish? For reasons such as these most New Zealand local authorities do not allow overnight camping outside of designated and approved areas. Where it is permitted, 'free camping' is usually limited to self-contained vehicles.

'Freedom camping' is becoming much less common in New Zealand so always check with the local visitor information centre about the relevant district council's policy. The Central Hawke's Bay and Gisborne district councils are two of the few councils still allowing 'freedom camping'. This atlas does not attempt to define areas for 'free camping' unless they have been designated so by the appropriate authorities.

The 'trade-off' of such 'free camping' is that the campers bring shopping revenue to the community, and their overnight presence may mean there is less vandalism in the immediate area.

Perhaps the last word on 'free camping' should come from the NZMCA's code of ethics which requires members to: "be discreet when choosing an overnight parking or camping spot – consider how the surrounding neighbours may react," and also to "respect restrictions for length of stay - do not overstay your welcome. If asked to move on, do so gracefully."

Destination Fiordland

Mitre Peak, Milford Sound

A guide to considerate Kiwi camping

- Be discreet when choosing an overnight parking or camping spot, and if it is not in a designated camp always ask permission where possible.
- Park your vehicle, or pitch your tent, with safety in mind. Consider the possibilities of overnight strong winds, flooding (streams can rise very quickly) and fire as well as security.
- Keep your campsite clean and tidy, and try to leave it even tidier than when you found it.
- Dispose of all your wastewater and rubbish in a sanitary and approved manner.
- Avoid causing visual or sound pollution. For example, use generators and stereos etc only at appropriate times during the day, and don't hang washing in places that may offend others.
- Observe all local fire restrictions and when appropriate use only existing fireplaces and/or portable BBQs.
- Ensure your vehicle is roadworthy and meets all relevant regulations.
- Be a considerate and safe driver, and obey road safety rules. If travelling slowly or sightseeing, keep an eye on your rear vision mirror and pull over to let others pass.
- Comply with local animal control bylaws. Preferably either leave your pets at home or in care, but if you must travel with them, keep your pets under control and pick up after them.
- Respect restrictions for length of stay. If asked to move on, do so graciously.
- Water, power, waste disposal, and road and ground maintenance all cost money and the days of 'free camping' are fast disappearing. So be prepared to pay a reasonable contribution or donation to keep such facilities available.

Mount Taranaki

Destination Taranaki

Travelling with a pet

The following are general guides to follow if you do decide to travel with your pet:

- Not all camping grounds welcome pets - if in doubt ring and check before you arrive. Pets are not welcome in Department of Conservation areas.
- A current hydatids certificate should be carried.
- Parvovirus inoculation certificates may be required in some areas.
- Pets should be exercised out of the camp area twice a day or more.
- Pets should be supervised and under control at all times.
- Pets should not be left unattended while owners are absent.
- Always clean up after your pet – many local authorities have substantial fines for inappropriate littering.

Toilet hygiene

The disposal of human waste into natural waters is not only dangerous to our health, it is extremely offensive to Maori cultural and spiritual concerns.

To protect your own health and the environment while travelling in New Zealand:

- Always use the public toilets provided where possible.
- Dispose of all caravan and campervan toilet wastes in appropriate and approved facilities. Such 'dump stations' are clearly signposted throughout New Zealand.
- If toilets are not available, bury your toilet waste at least 100m from picnic areas, camp-sites and waterways and at least 15cm deep.

Tourism West Coast

Jacksons Bay, West Coast

Drinking water

While once the majority of water found in New Zealand rivers was pure and drinkable; it is now relatively common to see signs warning "this water is not suitable for drinking". The parasite Giardia has been found in some New Zealand lakes, rivers and streams and can cause severe diarrhoea. Giardia lives in the intestine of mammals and can be spread when toilet waste is not buried or is buried close to a stream, lake or well.

Despite this relatively new threat, water suited for drinking is readily available throughout New Zealand via most public taps, or you may prefer to purchase bottled water. If in doubt, ask the locals if the water is safe for drinking.

Water taken from streams and rivers can be made safe in three ways:

- Boil for three minutes
- Add an iodine solution or chlorine bleach (available from a pharmacy)
- Filter water through a suitable Giardia-rated filter, available from most outdoor equipment shops

Alexandra

Photo Tourism Central Otago

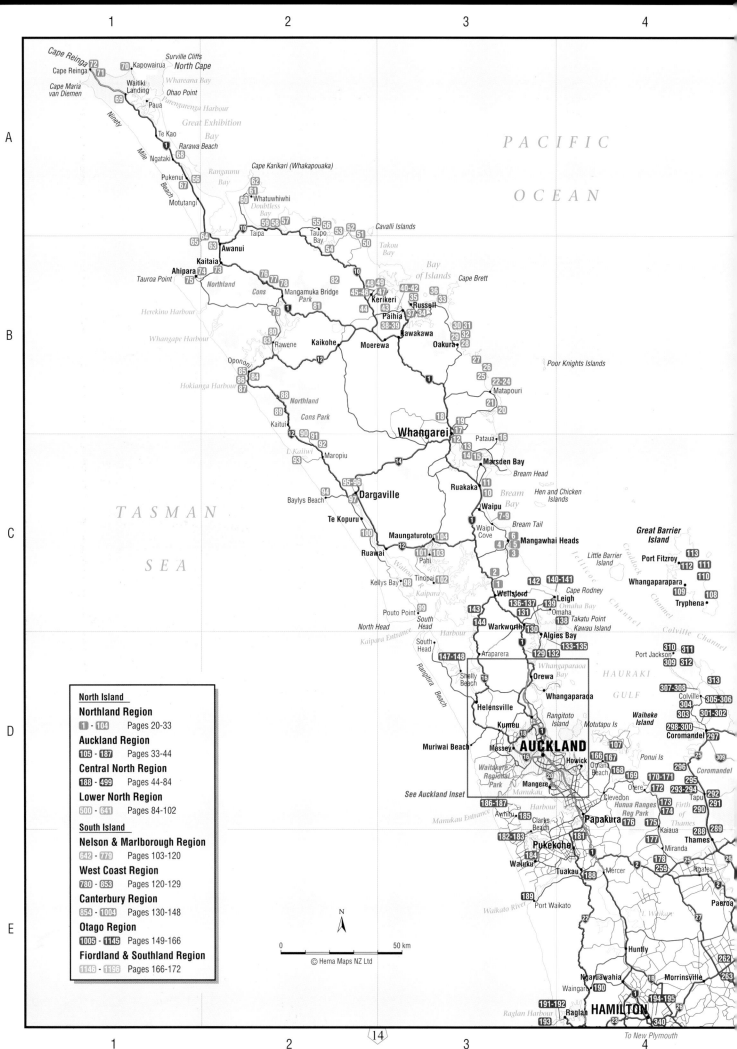

© Hema Maps NZ Ltd

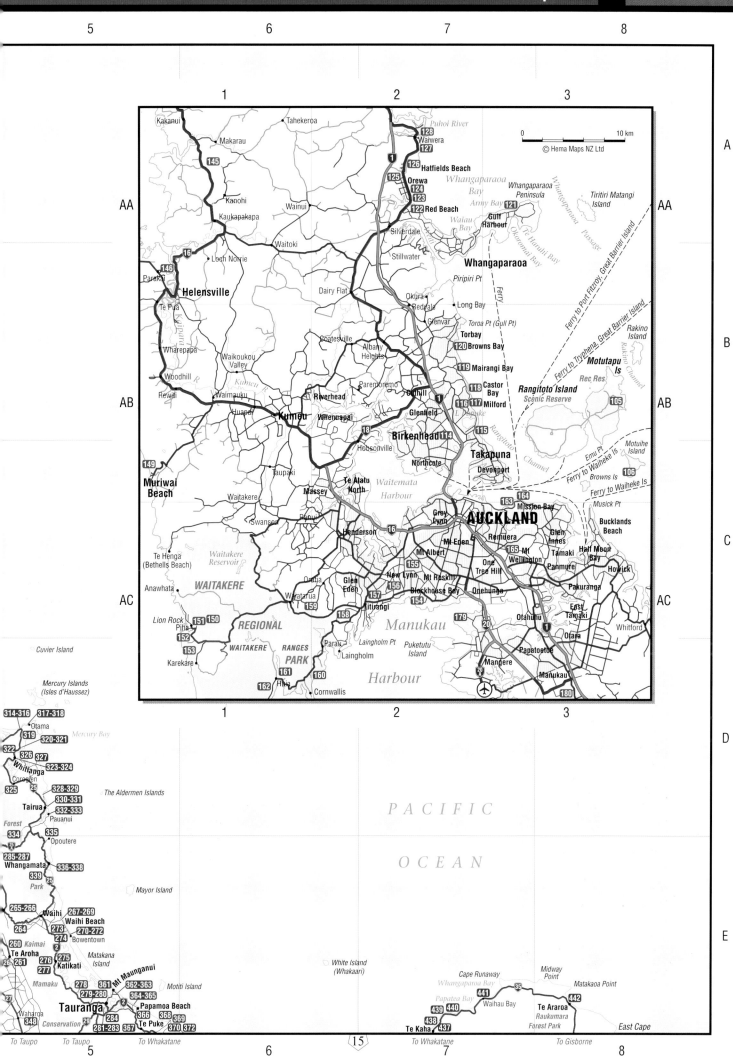

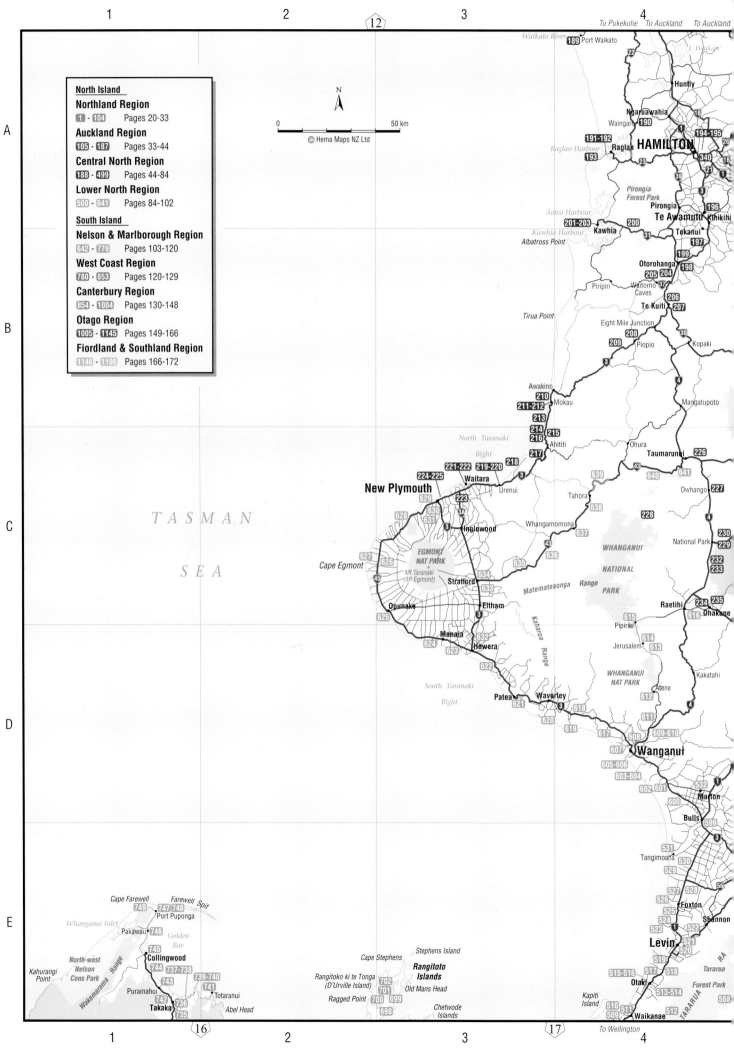

North Island

Northland Region
1 - 104   Pages 20-33

Auckland Region
105 - 187   Pages 33-44

Central North Region
188 - 499   Pages 44-84

Lower North Region
500 - 641   Pages 84-102

South Island

Nelson & Marlborough Region
642 - 779   Pages 103-120

West Coast Region
780 - 853   Pages 120-129

Canterbury Region
854 - 1004   Pages 130-148

Otago Region
1005 - 1145   Pages 149-166

Fiordland & Southland Region
1146 - 1196   Pages 166-172

N

0   50 km

© Hema Maps NZ Ltd

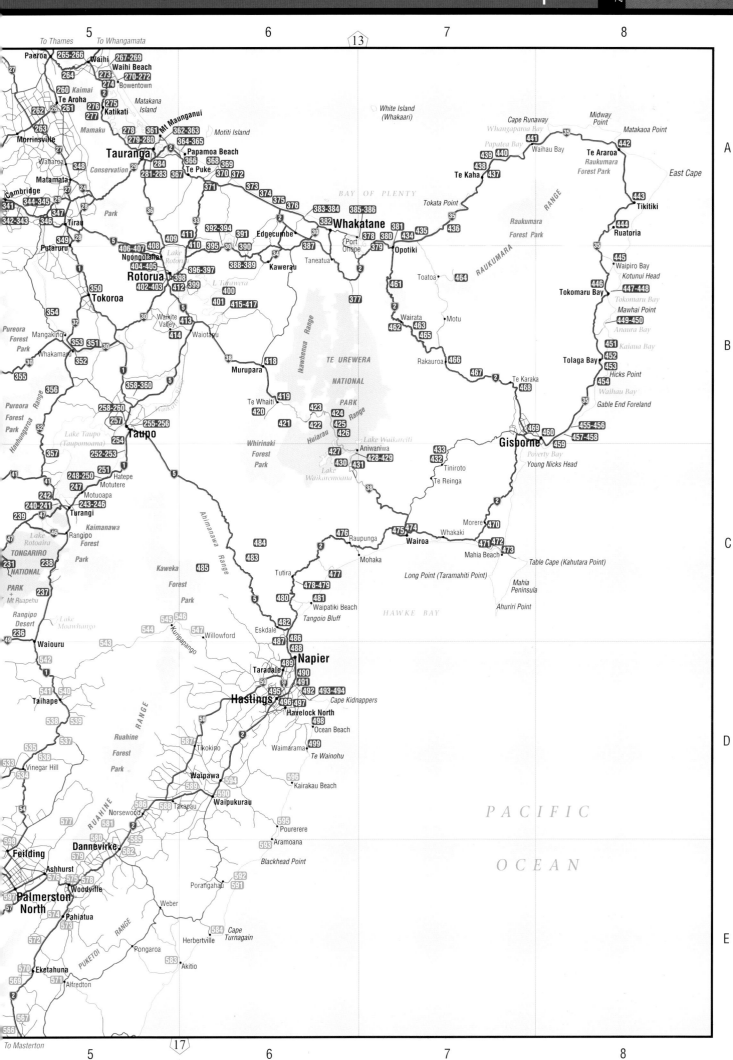

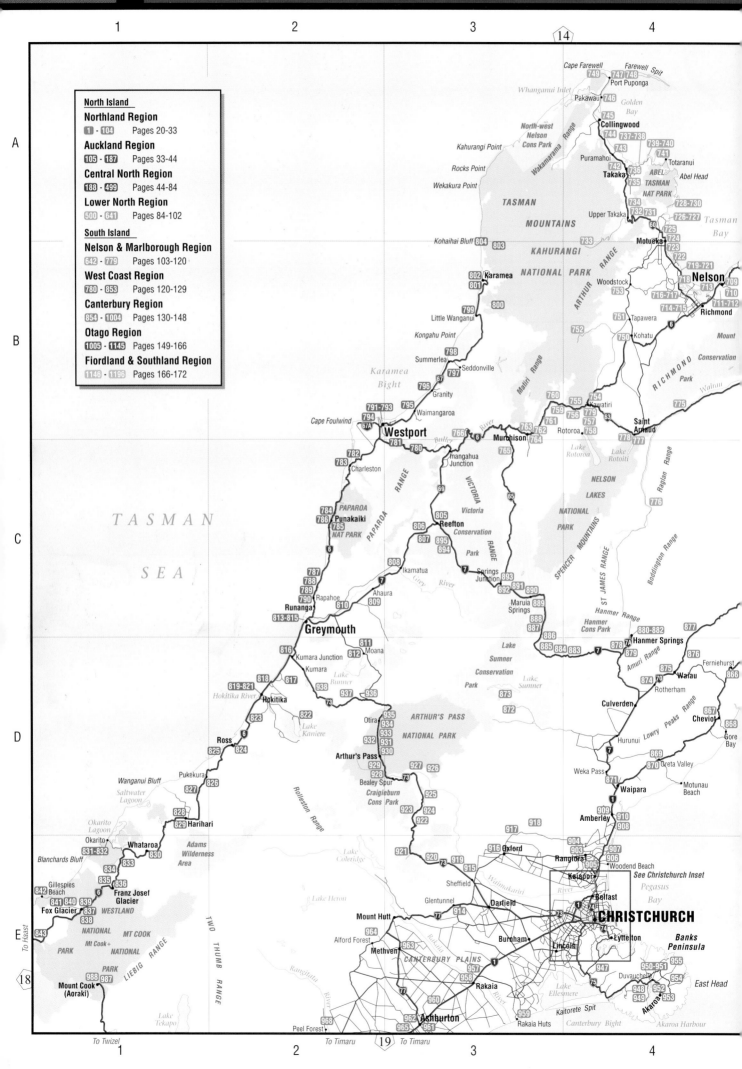

North Island

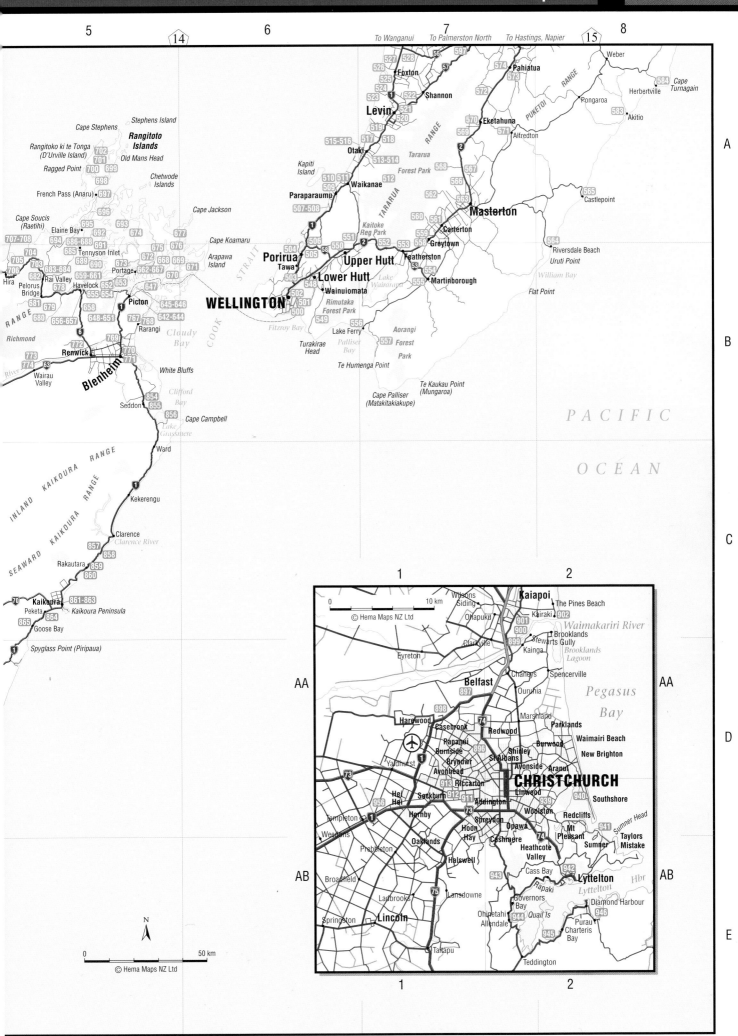

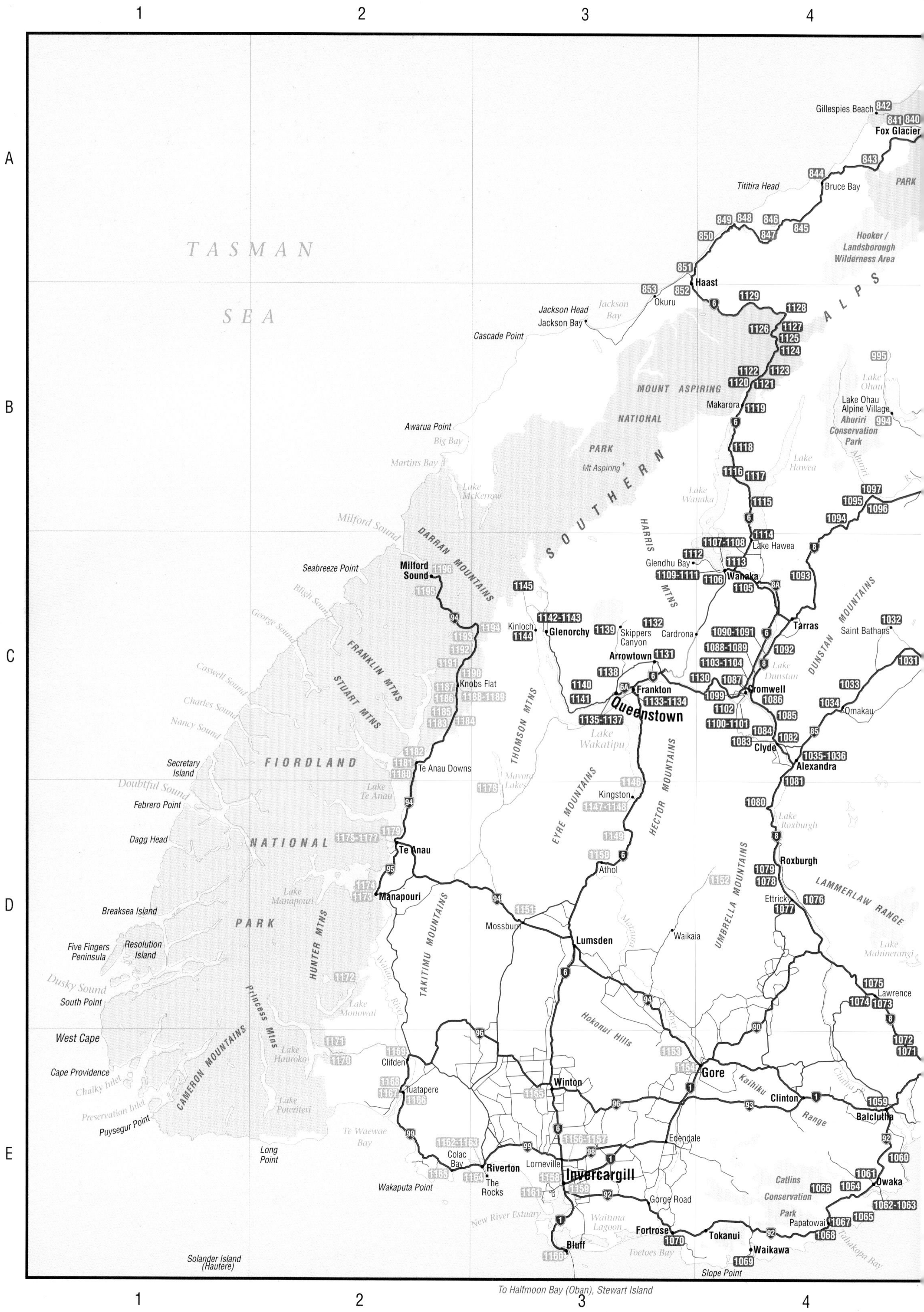
1
2
3
4
A
B
C
D
E
TASMAN
SEA
Gillespies Beach
Fox Glacier
Titira Head
Bruce Bay
PARK
Hooker / Landsborough Wilderness Area
Haast
Okuru
Jackson Head
Jackson Bay
Cascade Point
SOUTHERN ALPS
MOUNT ASPIRING NATIONAL PARK
Mt Aspiring
Makarora
Lake Ohau
Lake Ohau Alpine Village
Ahuriri Conservation Park
Lake Hawea
Lake Wanaka
Awarua Point
Big Bay
Martins Bay
Lake McKerrow
Milford Sound
DARRAN MOUNTAINS
HARRIS MTNS
Lake Hawea
Glendhu Bay
Wanaka
Seabreeze Point
Bligh Sound
George Sound
FRANKLIN MTNS
STUART MTNS
Kinloch
Glenorchy
Skippers Canyon
Cardrona
Tarras
DUNSTAN MOUNTAINS
Saint Bathans
Caswell Sound
Charles Sound
Nancy Sound
Knobs Flat
Arrowtown
Frankton
Queenstown
Cromwell
Lake Dunstan
Omakau
Lake Wakatipu
Clyde
Alexandra
Secretary Island
FIORDLAND
Te Anau Downs
THOMSON MTNS
Mavora Lakes
Doubtful Sound
Febrero Point
Lake Te Anau
EYRE MOUNTAINS
HECTOR MOUNTAINS
Kingston
Lake Roxburgh
Dagg Head
NATIONAL
Te Anau
Athol
Roxburgh
LAMMERLAW RANGE
Manapouri
Lake Manapouri
UMBRELLA MOUNTAINS
Ettrick
Breaksea Island
PARK
Mossburn
Waikaia
Lumsden
Five Fingers Peninsula
Resolution Island
HUNTER MTNS
TAKITIMU MOUNTAINS
Lake Mahinerangi
Dusky Sound
South Point
Princess Mtns
Lake Monowai
Lawrence
West Cape
CAMERON MOUNTAINS
Hokonui Hills
Lake Hauroko
Clifden
Gore
Cape Providence
Chalky Inlet
Kaihiku Range
Tuatapere
Winton
Clinton
Preservation Inlet
Lake Poteriteri
Puysegur Point
Balclutha
Te Waewae Bay
Edendale
Long Point
Colac Bay
Riverton
Lorneville
Invercargill
Owaka
Wakaputa Point
The Rocks
Catlins Conservation Park
Gorge Road
New River Estuary
Papatowai
Waituna Lagoon
Fortrose
Tokanui
Bluff
Waikawa
Toetoes Bay
Tahakopa Bay
Solander Island (Hautere)
Slope Point
To Halfmoon Bay (Oban), Stewart Island

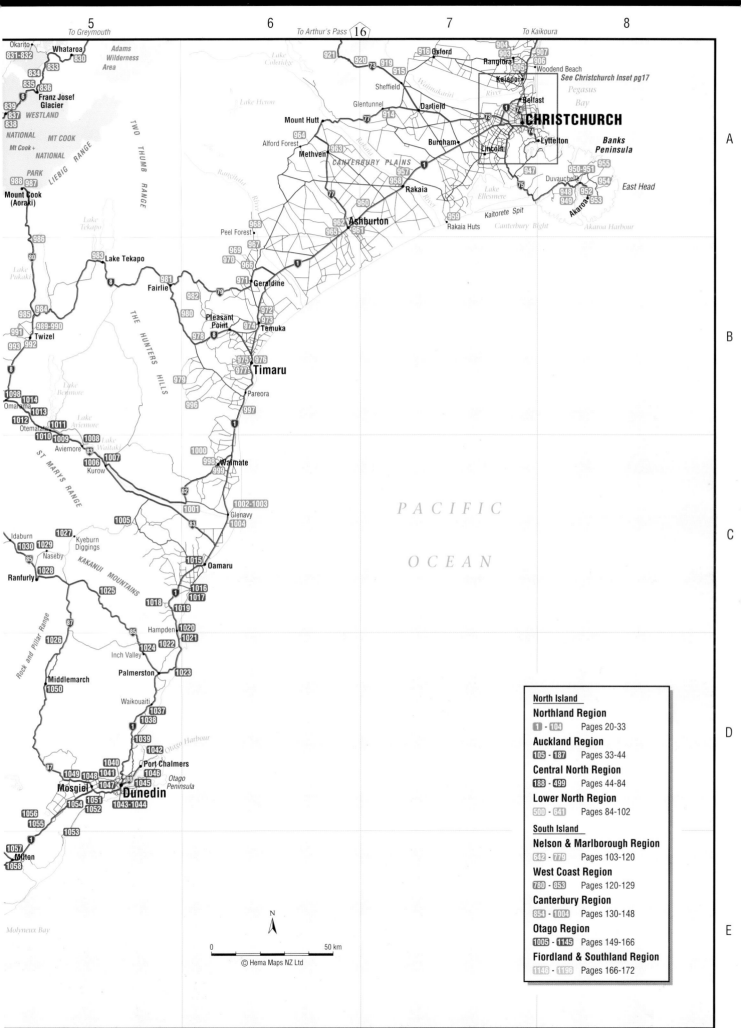

North Island

Northland Region
1 - 104   Pages 20-33

Auckland Region
105 - 187   Pages 33-44

Central North Region
188 - 499   Pages 44-84

Lower North Region
500 - 641   Pages 84-102

South Island

Nelson & Marlborough Region
642 - 779   Pages 103-120

West Coast Region
780 - 853   Pages 120-129

Canterbury Region
854 - 1004   Pages 130-148

Otago Region
1005 - 1145   Pages 149-166

Fiordland & Southland Region
1146 - 1198   Pages 166-172

© Hema Maps NZ Ltd

0   50 km

N

NORTHLAND REGION

Matai Bay

SH1 — Wellsford to Whangarei

1

Map 12 C3

Roadside Rest Area

Alongside SH1 N of Wellsford

2647100E 6549800N
Hema Atlas Map Ref 6 D8

2

Map 12 C3

Roadside Rest Area

Adjoining SH1 7km from Wellsford

2646900E 6551400N
Hema Atlas Map Ref 6 C8

3

Map 12 C3

Riverside Holiday Park

41 Black Swamp Rd, Mangawhai, off Mangawhai Rd:
signposted from the Mangawhai village centre
Ph/Fax (09) 431 4825 riverside.goodlife@xtra.co.nz

Author's note — Well managed and sheltered site set
in established grounds.

2653700E 6562000N
Hema Atlas Map Ref 6 B9

4

Map 12 C3

Mangawhai Village Holiday Park

71 Moir St: beside the main road at the
S end of Mangawhai village
Ph/Fax (09) 431 4542 bill@mvhp.co.nz

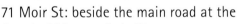
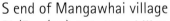

2651300E 6563300N
Hema Atlas Map Ref 6 B9

5

Map 12 C3

Hideaway Holiday Park

28 Moir Point Rd: signposted from Mangawhai
Ph (09) 431 4251 www.holidayparks.co.nz/mangbeach

Author's note — Sheltered and compact site with access
to the estuary.

2653600E 65640007N
Hema Atlas Map Ref 6 B9

6

Map 12 C3

Mangawhai Heads Motor Camp

Off Cove Rd: beachside at Mangawhai Heads
Ph (09) 431 4675

A caretaker will collect modest fees. Author's note — Popular waterfront
location has a huge camp on the waterfront with good shelter.

2654300E 6566900N
Hema Atlas Map Ref 6 B9

7

Map 12 C3

Roadside Rest Area

Off Cove Rd: S end of Waipu Beach

Author's note — waterside picnic spot is a popular beach with good surfing.

2647100E 6573900N
Hema Atlas Map Ref 6 A8

8

Map 12 C3

Camp Waipu Cove

Cove Rd, Waipu Cove: signposted from Beach Rd
Ph (09) 432 0410 info@campwaipucove.com

A huge camp right on the beach at this very popular spot.

2646000E 6574900N
Hema Atlas Map Ref 6 A8

9

Map 12 C3

Waipu Cove Cottages & Camp

Cove Rd, Waipu: Signposted from the Beach Rd
Ph/Fax (09) 432 0851 covecottages@xtra.co.nz

Author's note — Compact and immaculate.

2646000E 6574900N
Hema Atlas Map Ref 6 A8

10

Map 12 C3

Uretiti

Adjoining SH1 at Uretiti: 34km S of Whangarei
DoC Whangarei Area Office Ph (09) 430 2133
whangareivc@doc.govt.nz

Self registration applies; cold showers only.
Author's note — Beachside, but pretty exposed.

2642700E 6584500N
Hema Atlas Map Ref 4 J13

11

Map 12 C3

Ruakaka Reserve Motor Camp

21 Beach Rd, Ruakaka: signposted from SH1
Ph (09) 432 7590 ruakaka@ihug.co.nz

Author's note — A large and popular camp right on the beach with plenty of shelter and access to the nearby estuary.

2642100E 6587900N
Hema Atlas Map Ref 4 J13

12

Map 12 C3

Alpha Motel & Holiday Park

Adjoining SH1, S of Whangarei
Ph (09) 438 6600 info@alphaholidaypark.co.nz

2629700E 6607500N
Hema Atlas Ref 84 C1, 85 C1, 4 G11

13

Map 12 C3

Roadside Rest Area

Whangarei Heads Rd, Waikaraka on Whangarei Harbour

Author's note — waterside picnic spot.

2635900E 6602700N
Hema Atlas Map Ref 4 G12

14

Map 12 C3

Roadside Rest Area

Devonshire Park, Whangarei Heads Rd

Author's note — waterside picnic spot.

2637400E 6600900N
Hema Atlas Map Ref 4 G12

15

Map 12 C3

Blue Heron Holiday Park
Scott Rd; signposted from the Whangarei Heads Rd
Ph (09) 436 2293

Author's note — Small but scenic waterside spot.

2638600E 6600500N
Hema Atlas Map Ref 4 G12

16

Map 12 C3

Treasure Island Trailer Park
Pataua Bay, off Whangarei Heads Rd
Ph (09) 436 2390 treasure@xtra.co.nz

Author's note — Huge park-like grounds with dual waterfront access: open sea or estuary.

2649700E 6608200N
Hema Atlas Map Ref 4 G13

SH1 — Whangarei to Kawakawa

17

Map 12 B3

Whangarei Top 10 Holiday Park
24 Mair St, Whangarei: signposted from SH1 on
the N side of Whangarei city centre
Ph 0800 455 488 stay@whangareitop10.co.nz

Author's note — Wooded location next to stream and scenic reserve.

2630100E 6609700N
Hema Atlas Map Ref 85 B2, 4 G11

18

Map 12 B3

Kamo Springs Holiday Park
Adjoining SH1, approx 7km N of Whangarei
Ph/Fax (09) 435 1208 kamosprings@xtra.co.nz

2627200E 6614000N
Hema Atlas Map Ref 85 A1, 4 F11

19

Map 12 B3

Roadside Rest Area
Whangarei Falls Scenic Reserve, off Ngunguru Rd

2632500E 6611900N
Hema Atlas Map Ref 85 A2, 4 F12

20

Map 12 B3

Roadside Rest Area
Roadside S of Tutukaka, off Ngunguru Rd

2648700E 6618500N
Hema Atlas Map Ref 4 F13

21

Map 12 B3

Tutukaka Holiday Park
Matapouri Rd, Tutukaka: at the N end of Tutukaka township
Ph/Fax (09) 434 3938 tutsholidaypk@igrin.co.nz

Author's note — Short walk to Tutukaka's marinas and wharf from this clean and tidy camp.

2648000E 6620400N
Hema Atlas Map Ref 4 E13

22

Map 12 B3

Roadside Rest Area
Whale Bay, off Matapouri Rd

Author's note — waterside picnic spot.

2646800E 6626000N
Hema Atlas Map Ref 4 E13

Roadside Rest Area

23

Woolleys Bay, off Matapouri Rd

Map 12 B3   Author's note — waterside picnic spot.

2645600E 6626300N

Hema Atlas Map Ref 4 E13

Roadside Rest Area

24

Sandy Bay, off Matapouri Rd

Map 12 B3   Author's note — waterside picnic spot.

2644400E 6626700N

Hema Atlas Map Ref 4 E13

Whananaki Nth Motel & Holiday Park

25

Signposted on entering Whananaki

Ph/Fax (09) 433 8896 whananaki@igrin.co.nz

Map 12 B3   This camp was for sale in 2006, so check status before arriving.

2642400E 6631700N

Hema Atlas Map Ref 4 D13

Otamure Beach

26

Beachside at Otamure on Whananaki North Rd,
just 2km from Whananaki
DoC Whangarei Area Office Ph (09) 430 2133
whangareivc@doc.govt.nz

Map 12 B3

Self registration applies; cold showers only.
Author's note — Beachside in a beautiful location, a good alternative
if Whananaki Holiday Park is not available.

2643800E 6633800N

Hema Atlas Map Ref 4 D13

Waikahoa Bay, Mimiwhangata Coastal Park

27

Mimiwhangata Coastal Park, 48km NE of Whangarei
DoC Whangarei Area Office Ph (09) 430 2133
whangareivc@doc.govt.nz

Map 12 B3   Closed June 1 to October 31; bookings required for peak season;
cold showers only

2639800E 6637500N

Hema Atlas Map Ref 4 D12

Oakura Motels & Holiday Park

28

Te Rapua St, Oakura Bay: off Russell Rd
Ph/Fax (09) 433 6803 oakuramotelsandhp@xtra.co.nz

Map 12 B3   Author's note — Sheltered site is just back from the beach.

2633500E 6644800N

Hema Atlas Map Ref 4 C12

Whangaruru Beachfront Camp

29

Just N of the Oakura township

A caretaker may collect koha or fees if they are in attendance.
Map 12 B3   Author's note — Beachside, and just a stone's throw from Oakura.

2632400E 6646500N

Hema Atlas Map Ref 4 C12

Bland Bay DoC Reserve

30

Whangaruru North Head Rd, Bland Bay

Map 12 B3

2633500E 6650900N

Hema Atlas Map Ref 4 B12

31 Bland Bay Motor Camp

Whangaruru North Head Rd, Bland Bay

Map 12 B3

A caretaker may collect koha or fees if they are in attendance.

2634700E 6650900N
Hema Atlas Map Ref 4 B12

32 Whangaruru North Head, Whangaruru Scenic Reserve

Whangaruru North Head Rd, 30km SE of Russell;
signposted from Bland Bay
DoC Russell Visitor Centre Ph (09) 403 9005
russellvc@doc.govt.nz

Map 12 B3

Bookings required in peak season; foot access only July 1 - November 30;
casual camping self registration applies; cold showers only.
Author's note — Simple camping in a lovely environment, difficult to
choose between this and the nearby Bland Bay option.

2635100E 6647700N
Hema Atlas Map Ref 4 C12

33 Roadside Rest Area & picnic area

Rawhiti Beach, off Russell Rd

Map 12 B3

Local Iwi allow some simple camping, but make sure you ask
permission, and be prepared to pay some koha.

2624800E 6662400N
Hema Atlas Map Ref 4 A11

34 Orongo Bay Holiday Park

Russell Rd, approx 2km S of Russell
Ph (09) 403 7704 orongobayholidaypark@xtra.co.nz

Map 12 B3

Author's note — Sheltered valley that's handy to boat ramps.

2616000E 6657000N
Hema Atlas Map Ref 81 B3, 4 B10

35 Russell Top 10 Holiday Park

Longbeach Rd, Russell: signposted to the
N of Russell town centre
Ph 0800 148 671 russelltop10@xtra.co.nz

Map 12 B3

Only 800m from Russell town centre.

2613500E 6660200N
Hema Atlas Ref 82 A5, 81 A3, 4 B10

36 Urupukapuka Island

Cable Bay, Urupukapuka Island: NE of Russell
(boat access only)
DoC Russell Visitor Centre Ph (09) 403 9009
russellvc@doc.govt.nz

Map 12 B3

Bookings required; cold showers only

2622600E 6664400N
Hema Atlas Map Ref 4 A11

37 Beachside Holiday Park

SH11, 4km S of Paihia
Ph (09) 402 7678 beachsideholiday@xtra.co.nz

Map 12 B3

Author's note — Compact and beachside.

2611500E 6655500N
Hema Atlas Map Ref 81 C2, 4 B10

38 Roadside Rest Area

Paihia

Map 12 B3

Author's note — Several waterside picnic spots in this area.

2610000E 6658100N
Hema Atlas Ref 83 C4, 81 B2, 4 B9

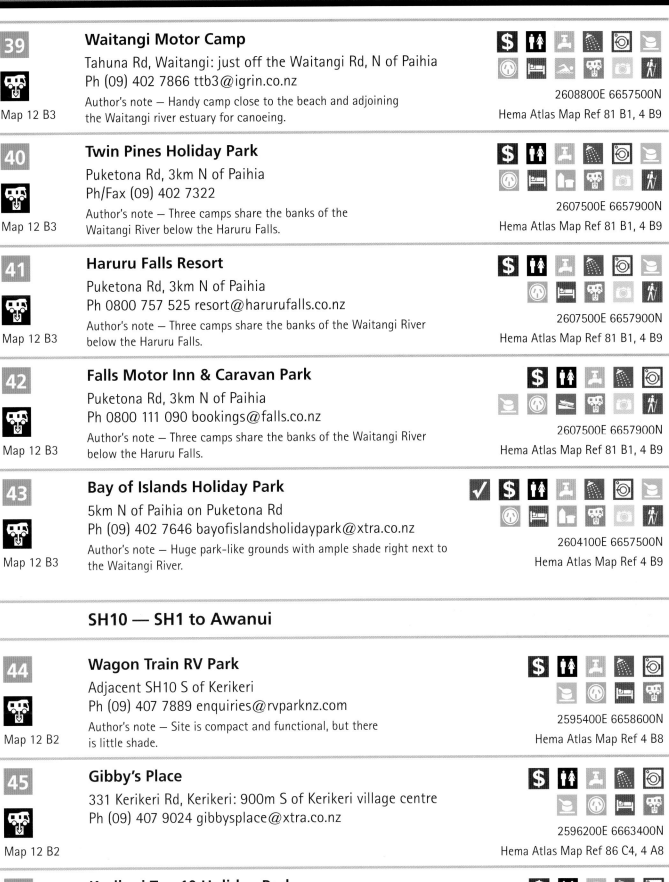

39

Map 12 B3

Waitangi Motor Camp

Tahuna Rd, Waitangi: just off the Waitangi Rd, N of Paihia
Ph (09) 402 7866 ttb3@igrin.co.nz
Author's note — Handy camp close to the beach and adjoining
the Waitangi river estuary for canoeing.

2608800E 6657500N
Hema Atlas Map Ref 81 B1, 4 B9

40

Map 12 B3

Twin Pines Holiday Park

Puketona Rd, 3km N of Paihia
Ph/Fax (09) 402 7322
Author's note — Three camps share the banks of the
Waitangi River below the Haruru Falls.

2607500E 6657900N
Hema Atlas Map Ref 81 B1, 4 B9

41

Map 12 B3

Haruru Falls Resort

Puketona Rd, 3km N of Paihia
Ph 0800 757 525 resort@harurufalls.co.nz
Author's note — Three camps share the banks of the Waitangi River
below the Haruru Falls.

2607500E 6657900N
Hema Atlas Map Ref 81 B1, 4 B9

42

Map 12 B3

Falls Motor Inn & Caravan Park

Puketona Rd, 3km N of Paihia
Ph 0800 111 090 bookings@falls.co.nz
Author's note — Three camps share the banks of the Waitangi River
below the Haruru Falls.

2607500E 6657900N
Hema Atlas Map Ref 81 B1, 4 B9

43

Map 12 B3

Bay of Islands Holiday Park

5km N of Paihia on Puketona Rd
Ph (09) 402 7646 bayofislandsholidaypark@xtra.co.nz
Author's note — Huge park-like grounds with ample shade right next to
the Waitangi River.

2604100E 6657500N
Hema Atlas Map Ref 4 B9

SH10 — SH1 to Awanui

44

Map 12 B2

Wagon Train RV Park

Adjacent SH10 S of Kerikeri
Ph (09) 407 7889 enquiries@rvparknz.com
Author's note — Site is compact and functional, but there
is little shade.

2595400E 6658600N
Hema Atlas Map Ref 4 B8

45

Map 12 B2

Gibby's Place

331 Kerikeri Rd, Kerikeri: 900m S of Kerikeri village centre
Ph (09) 407 9024 gibbysplace@xtra.co.nz

2596200E 6663400N
Hema Atlas Map Ref 86 C4, 4 A8

46

Map 12 B2

Kerikeri Top 10 Holiday Park

Aranga Drive, Kerikeri: 800m S of Kerikeri village centre
Ph 0800 272 642 mail@kerikeritop10.co.nz

2596200E 6663400N
Hema Atlas Map Ref 86 C4, 4 A8

47 Map 12 B3

Pagoda Lodge
81 Pa Road, Kerikeri: signposted from Kerikeri village centre
Ph (09) 407 8617 info@pagoda.co.nz
Author's note — Powered sites and pre-pitched tents
in a tranquil setting.

2599100E 6663800N
Hema Atlas Map Ref 86 B6, 4 A8

48 Map 12 B2

Rest Area, Rainbow Falls Scenic Reserve
Signposted from N access road to Kerikeri

Walking, swimming

2597100E 6664800N
Hema Atlas Map Ref 86 B4, 4 A8

49 Map 12 B3

Kerikeri Stone House DoC Reserve
Just N of the Stone House, Kerikeri

Walking, swimming

2598300E 6665300N
Hema Atlas Map Ref 86 B5, 4 A8

50 Map 12 B2

Matauri Bay Holiday Park
Beachside at Matauri Bay: along the scenic coastal route
Ph/Fax (09) 405 0525 matauribayhp@actrix.co.nz

Surfing, diving Author's note — Dust from the gravel access road.

2593400E 6685400N
Hema Atlas Map Ref 2 H12

51 Map 12 A2

Roadside Rest Area
Te Ngaere Bay: along the scenic coastal route

Author's note — waterside picnic spot.

2590500E 6686800N
Hema Atlas Map Ref 2 H12

52 Map 12 A2

Wainui Whanau Holiday Park
Roadside at Wainui: along the scenic coastal route

A caretaker may collect koha or fees if they are in attendance.
Seek permission before camping.

2589300E 6687700N
Hema Atlas Map Ref 2 H11

53 Map 12 A2

Tauranga Bay Holiday Park & Roadside Rest Area
Tauranga Beach: a 3km diversion from the coastal scenic
route. Ph/Fax (09) 405 0436 holiday@igrin.co.nz
Author's note — At a very pretty beach, but a tad exposed to the
sun as there's little shade.

2583400E 6688700N
Hema Atlas Map Ref 2 H11

54 Map 12 B2

Whangaroa Harbour Holiday Park
Whangaroa Harbour, along the coastal scenic route:
6km N of SH10. Ph (09) 405 0306

Fishing Author's note — Right next to the harbour in a sheltered valley.

2579600E 6681600N
Hema Atlas Map Ref 2 H10

55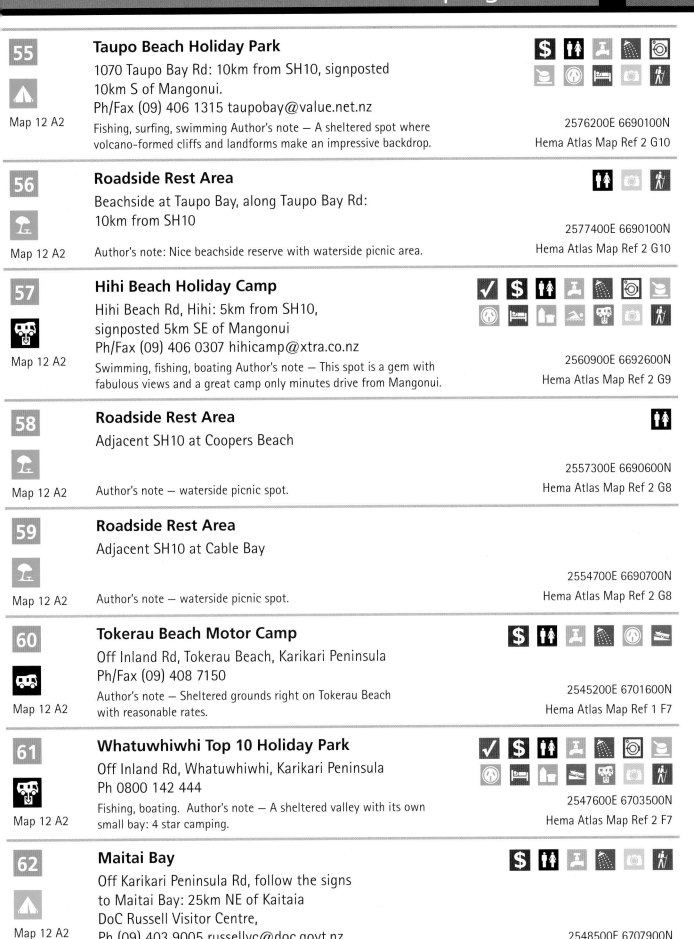

Map 12 A2

Taupo Beach Holiday Park

1070 Taupo Bay Rd: 10km from SH10, signposted
10km S of Mangonui.
Ph/Fax (09) 406 1315 taupobay@value.net.nz

Fishing, surfing, swimming Author's note — A sheltered spot where
volcano-formed cliffs and landforms make an impressive backdrop.

2576200E 6690100N

Hema Atlas Map Ref 2 G10

56

Map 12 A2

Roadside Rest Area

Beachside at Taupo Bay, along Taupo Bay Rd:
10km from SH10

Author's note: Nice beachside reserve with waterside picnic area.

2577400E 6690100N

Hema Atlas Map Ref 2 G10

57

Map 12 A2

Hihi Beach Holiday Camp

Hihi Beach Rd, Hihi: 5km from SH10,
signposted 5km SE of Mangonui
Ph/Fax (09) 406 0307 hihicamp@xtra.co.nz

Swimming, fishing, boating Author's note — This spot is a gem with
fabulous views and a great camp only minutes drive from Mangonui.

2560900E 6692600N

Hema Atlas Map Ref 2 G9

58

Map 12 A2

Roadside Rest Area

Adjacent SH10 at Coopers Beach

Author's note — waterside picnic spot.

2557300E 6690600N

Hema Atlas Map Ref 2 G8

59

Map 12 A2

Roadside Rest Area

Adjacent SH10 at Cable Bay

Author's note — waterside picnic spot.

2554700E 6690700N

Hema Atlas Map Ref 2 G8

60

Map 12 A2

Tokerau Beach Motor Camp

Off Inland Rd, Tokerau Beach, Karikari Peninsula
Ph/Fax (09) 408 7150

Author's note — Sheltered grounds right on Tokerau Beach
with reasonable rates.

2545200E 6701600N

Hema Atlas Map Ref 1 F7

61

Map 12 A2

Whatuwhiwhi Top 10 Holiday Park

Off Inland Rd, Whatuwhiwhi, Karikari Peninsula
Ph 0800 142 444

Fishing, boating. Author's note — A sheltered valley with its own
small bay: 4 star camping.

2547600E 6703500N

Hema Atlas Map Ref 2 F7

62

Map 12 A2

Maitai Bay

Off Karikari Peninsula Rd, follow the signs
to Maitai Bay: 25km NE of Kaitaia
DoC Russell Visitor Centre,
Ph (09) 403 9005 russellvc@doc.govt.nz

Self registration applies; cold showers only; fishing, diving

2548500E 6707900N

Hema Atlas Map Ref 2 F7

63

Map 12 B2

Norfolk Motels and Caravan Park

500m E of Awanui on SH10
Ph/Fax (09) 406 7515 norfolkmotels@xtra.co.nz

Author's note — Motels offering a sheltered rear paddock for campervans.

2533300E 6684000N

Hema Atlas Map Ref 1 H6

SH1 — Awanui to Cape Reinga

64

Map 12 B2

Roadside Rest Area

Off SH1 alongside Lake Ngatu, near Waipapakauri

Author's note — Waterside picnic spot is a popular spot for boating.

2528300E 6687000N

Hema Atlas Map Ref 1 H5

65

Map 12 B1

The Park Top 10, Ninety Mile Beach

5km W of SH1 at Waipapakauri Beach: signposted diversion
Ph (09) 406 7298 ninetymilebeach@xtra.co.nz

Author's note — Handy access to Ninety Mile Beach and a popular base for local anglers.

2526100E 6685500N

Hema Atlas Map Ref 1 H4

66

Map 12 A1

Wagener Holiday Park

3km E of SH1 at Houhora Heads, S of Pukenui: signposted diversion
Ph (09) 409 8564 wagenerpark@xtra.co.nz

Author's note — Beautiful sheltered spot that is well worth the diversion. This camp is popular with families, boaters and anglers.

2523600E 6708900N

Hema Atlas Map Ref 1 F5

67

Map 12 A1

Pukenui Holiday Park

Lamb Rd, Pukenui: signposted W of SH1 at the centre of Pukenui
Ph (09) 409 8803 pukenuiholidays@xtra.co.nz

2521600E 6708400N

Hema Atlas Map Ref 1 F5

68

Map 12 A1

Rarawa

Rarawa Beach Rd; signposted E of SH1 N of Pukenui
DoC Russell Visitor Centre
Ph (09) 403 9005 russellvc@doc.govt.nz

Casual camping self registration applies; cold showers only.
Author's note — Beautiful beachside location, but the entrance sign is a little confusing — take the right fork for camping.

2518100E 6719100N

Hema Atlas Map Ref 1 E4

69

Map 12 A1

Waitiki Landing Holiday Complex

SH1 at Waitiki Landing
Ph/Fax (09) 409 7508 waitiki.landing@xtra.co.nz

Author's note — Small, functional camp that's the closest serviced camp to Cape Reinga.

2495400E 6741700N

Hema Atlas Map Ref 1 B2

70 | Map 12 A1

Kapowairua (Spirits Bay), Te Paki Recreation Reserve

Spirits Bay Rd, 16km from Waitiki Landing on SH1
DoC Russell Visitor Centre Ph (09) 403 9009
russellvc@doc.govt.nz
Cold showers only

2497200E 6753200N
Hema Atlas Map Ref 1 A2

---

71 | Map 12 A1

Tapotupotu

On Far North Rd: signposted from SH1 just S of
Cape Reinga, a 3km diversion.
DoC Russell Visitor Centre
Ph (09) 403 9005 russellvc@doc.govt.nz

Casual camping self registration applies; cold showers only.
Author's note — Don't leave Cape Reinga without visiting the
white sands of this magic bay.

2485500E 6752200N
Hema Atlas Map Ref 1 A1

---

72 | Map 12 A1

Roadside Rest Area

Cape Reinga

Author's note — Iconic and well worth the journey.

2482300E 6753300N
Hema Atlas Map Ref 1 A1

SH1 — Awanui to Kawakawa

73 | Map 12 B2

Kaitaia Motor Camp

Adjacent SH1 at the S end of Kaitaia
Enquiries to the shop Ph (09) 408 1212

Author's note — Functional, but not overly pretty.

2535100E 6674800N
Hema Atlas Map Ref 1 J6

---

74 | Map 12 B1

Ahipara Motor Camp & Lodge

Takahe St, signposted from Ahipara
Ph (09) 409 4864 pinetree@xtra.co.nz
Author's note — Nice location, just 800m from Ninety Mile Beach,
under the shade of pine trees.

2526300E 6671400N
Hema Atlas Map Ref 1 J5

---

75 | Map 12 B1

Te Kohania Camping Ground

Beachside at the end of Ahipara Bay

A caretaker may collect koha or fees if they are in attendance. Author's
note — Right on the coast at the favoured surf spot on this beach.

2522600E 6670000N
Hema Atlas Map Ref 1 J5

---

76 | Map 12 B2

Roadside Rest Area

Summit of the Mangamuka Saddle at 390m: along SH1

2552700E 6669100N
Hema Atlas Map Ref 2 K8

77

Map 12 B2

Roadside Rest Area
Mangamuka Gorge Scenic Reserve alongside SH1

Author's note — Waterside picnic area is a nice swimming spot.

2556300E 6667900N
Hema Atlas Map Ref 2 K8

78

Map 12 B2

Raetea North Side
Along SH1: north side of Raetea Range, beyond concrete ford
DoC Russell Visitor Centre Ph (09) 403 9009
russellvc@doc.govt.nz
Drinking water is from a stream

2557500E 6667000N
Hema Atlas Map Ref 2 K8

79

Map 12 B2

Hawkridge Farm Animal Farm
Along Kohukohu Rd: N of the Rawene Ferry landing

A caretaker may collect koha or fees if they are in attendance.
Only suited to self-contained campervans.

2557400E 6657000N
Hema Atlas Map Ref 3 B4

80

Map 12 B2

The Tree House
W of the Rawene Ferry's northern landing point

A caretaker may collect koha or fees if they are in attendance.
Author's note — Perhaps more suited to backpackers.

2558000E 6647700N
Hema Atlas Map Ref 3 C4

81

Map 12 B2

Forest Pools, Puketi Forest
Forest Road, Puketi Forest
DoC Russell Visitor Centre Ph (09) 403 9009
russellvc@doc.govt.nz
Camping only permitted overnight; drinking water is from a stream

2574300E 6657800N
Hema Atlas Map Ref 3 B6

82

Map 12 B2

Puketi Recreation Area
Waiare Rd, Puketi Forest: 20km NE of Okaihau
DoC Russell Visitor Centre Ph (09) 403 9009
russellvc@doc.govt.nz
Cold showers only; firewood provided

2581700E 6669200N
Hema Atlas Map Ref 3 A7

SH12 — SH1 to Dargaville

83

Map 12 B2

Rawene Motor Camp
1 Marmon St, Rawene: signposted from
Rawene Rd, off SH12
Ph/Fax (09) 405 1720 bobsmow@internet.co.nz
Author's note — Hillside camp with nice views of the Hokianga.

2555800E 6645200N
Hema Atlas Map Ref 3 C4

84

Map 12 B2

Opononi Beach Holiday Park
Adjacent SH12 at Opononi
Ph/Fax (09) 405 8791 harrybarlow@xtra.co.nz
Author's note — Opposite the magic beaches lining this part
of the Hokianga.

2547000E 6632200N
Hema Atlas Map Ref 3 D3

85
Map 12 B2

Roadside Rest Area

Along SH12 S of Opononi: several sites

Author's note — Camping is not allowed but there are several picnic spots right next to the white sand beaches of the Hokianga Harbour.

2545300E 6631400N
Hema Atlas Map Ref 3 D3

86
Map 12 B2

Roadside Rest Area

Arai-Te-Uru Recreation Reserve: signposted 800m from SH12

Author's note — Nice views over Hokianga Harbour and beach walks from this reserve — but no camping.

2544500E 6630100N
Hema Atlas Map Ref 3 D3

87
Map 12 B2

Roadside Rest Area

Pakia Hill, SH12: overlooking the entrance to the Hokianga Harbour

Author's note — Best approached from the S. This viewpoint provides memorable views of the famed Hokianga Harbour.

2545000E 6628500N
Hema Atlas Map Ref 3 E3

88
Map 12 B2

Tane Mahuta Reserve and Rest Area

Adjacent SH12, Waipoua Forest

Author's note — Take a short walk to view Tane Mahuta ('Lord of the Forest') — a revered kauri tree 4.4m in diameter, and thought to be 2000 years old.

2559300E 6622800N
Hema Atlas Map Ref 3 E4

89
Map 12 B2

Waipoua Forest DoC Visitor Centre and Camping Area

Waipoua River Rd, Waipoua Forest: signposted W of SH12
DoC Kauri Coast Visitor Centre Ph (09) 439 3011
kauricoastvc@doc.govt.nz

Self registration applies Author's note — Sheltered forest setting next to a nice stream.

2560400E 6617000N
Hema Atlas Map Ref 3 F4

90
Map 12 C2

Trounson Kauri Park

Donnellys Crossing Loop Rd: 40km N of Dargaville
DoC Kauri Coast Visitor Centre Ph (09) 439 3011
kauricoastvc@doc.govt.nz

Self registration applies; closed Easter to Labour Weekend.
Author's note — Located in a pretty valley with a stream.

2568900E 6608300N
Hema Atlas Map Ref 3 G5

91
Map 12 C2

Kauri Coast Top 10 Holiday Park

Trounson Park Rd: signposted to the E of SH12,
S of Waipoua Forest Park
Ph 0800 807 200 kauricoast.top10@xtra.co.nz

Author's note — Sheltered valley alongside a pretty swimming hole.

2572200E 6606100N
Hema Atlas Map Ref 3 G6

92
Map 12 C2

Pine Beach Campground, Kaiiwi Lakes

End of Campground Rd, off Kai Iwi Lakes Rd,
Taharoa Domain
Kauri Coast Information Centre, Dargaville
Ph (09) 439 8360

Cold showers only

2574500E 6603700N
Hema Atlas Map Ref 3 H6

93

Map 12 C2

Promenade Point Campground, Kaiiwi Lakes

Off Kai Iwi Lakes Rd, Taharoa Domain
Kauri Coast Information Centre, Dargaville
Ph (09) 439 8360

A caretaker may collect koha or fees if they are in attendance.
Author's note — White sand beaches line this freshwater lake, and pine trees provide shelter and shade making this a nice spot to stop.

2568000E 6598200N

Hema Atlas Map Ref 3 H5

94

Map 12 C2

Bayleys Beach Holiday Park

22 Seaview Rd, Bayleys Beach: 10km W of Dargaville
Ph/Fax (09) 439 6349 motorcamp@bayleysbeach.co.nz

Author's note — Just up the road from a nice West Coast beach.

2577600E 6584000N

Hema Atlas Map Ref 3 J6

SH12 — Dargaville to SH1

95

Map 12 C2

Dargaville Holiday Park

10 Onslow St, Dargaville: signposted from
SH12 E of Dargaville town centre
Ph 0800 114 441 dargavilleholidaypark@xtra.co.nz
Author's note — Neat and tidy with good facilities.

2589100E 6585400N

Hema Atlas Map Ref 3 J7

96

Map 12 C2

Dargaville Campervan Park & Cabins

18 Gladstone St, Dargaville: signposted from
Dargaville town centre
Ph/Fax (09) 439 8479 rayglen@xtra.co.nz
Author's note — Handy to the town centre but little more than a gravelled yard.

2589100E 6585400N

Hema Atlas Map Ref 3 J7

97

Map 12 C2

Roadside Rest Area

Near the town centre at Dargaville

Author's note — waterside picnic area.

2589800E 6583600N

Hema Atlas Map Ref 3 J7

98

Map 12 C3

Kellys Bay Motor Camp

Follow Pouto Rd off SH12 to Kellys Bay
Ph (09) 439 4204

2610000E 6549300N

Hema Atlas Map Ref 5 D4

99

Map 12 C3

Pouto Point Motor Camp

Follow Pouto Rd off SH12 to Pouto Point
Ph (09) 439 0199

2616800E 6537700N

Hema Atlas Map Ref 5 E5

100

Map 12 C2

Roadside Rest Area

Adjacent SH12, S of Dargaville

Author's note — waterside picnic area.

2597400E 6569900N

Hema Atlas Map Ref 5 B3

101 Matakohe Top 10 Holiday Park

Map 12 C3

Church Rd, Matakohe: follow the signs to the
Matakohe Kauri Museum
Ph 0800 431 6431 matakoheholidaypark@xtra.co.nz
Author's note — Compact, rural environment next door to the Kauri
Museum. Facilities can get a little pressured at peak times.

2618100E 6562700N
Hema Atlas Map Ref 5 B5

102 Tinopai Motor Camp

Map 12 C3

Komiti Rd, Tinopai: off SH12 at Matakohe
Ph (09) 431 6797

2623400E 6549200N
Hema Atlas Map Ref 5 D6

103 Pahi Beach Motor Camp

Map 12 C3

Beachside at Pahi Beach: 7km from SH12
Ph/Fax (09) 431 7322
Author's note: Worthwhile deviation to see old buildings
in a pretty harbourside location.

2621400E 6560700N
Hema Atlas Map Ref 5 B6

104 Paparoa Motor Camp

Map 12 C3

Cnr SH12 & Pahi Rd, Paparoa
Ph (09) 431 6515 paparoamotorcamp@xtra.co.nz
Author's note: New owners are breathing life back into this
conveniently located camp.

2622000E 6565000N
Hema Atlas Map Ref 5 B6

AUCKLAND REGION

Auckland Harbour

Islands of the Hauraki Gulf

105 Home Bay

Map 13 AB3

Motutapu Island, east coast (boat access only)
DoC Auckland Information Centre Ph (09) 379 6476
aucklandvc@doc.govt.nz

2682400E 6491700N
Hema Atlas Map Ref 7 C6

106 Motuihe Island

Motuihe Wharf, Wharf Bay, Motuihe Island
(boat access only)
DoC Auckland Information Centre Ph (09) 379 6476
aucklandvc@doc.govt.nz
Bookings required for boat access: Ph (09) 534 8095

2683700E 6485200N
Hema Atlas Map Ref 90 B6, 7 D6

107 Map 12 D4

Whakanewha Regional Park
Waiheke Island
Auckland Regional Council Ph (09) 366 2000 www.arc.govt.
nz info@arc.govt.nz
Bookings essential all year

2696600E 6484700N
Hema Atlas Map Ref 7 D7

---

108 Map 12 C4

Medlands Beach
S end of Medlands Beach, Great Barrier Island
(car ferry access)
DoC Great Barrier Island Area Office Ph (09) 429 0044
Bookings essential all year

2735600E 6544400N
Hema Atlas Map Ref 36 E5

---

109 Map 12 C4

The Green
Whangaparapara Harbour, Great Barrier Island
(car ferry access)
DoC Great Barrier Island Area Office Ph (09) 429 0044
Bookings essential all year

2722600E 6545600N
Hema Atlas Map Ref 36 E4

---

110 Map 12 C4

Awana Beach
Awana estuary, Great Barrier Island east coast
(car ferry access)
DoC Great Barrier Island Area Office Ph (09) 429 0044
Bookings essential all year

2732400E 6551600N
Hema Atlas Map Ref 36 D5

---

111 Map 12 C4

Harataonga
Kaitoke/Port Fitzroy Rd, Great Barrier Island
(car ferry access)
DoC Great Barrier Island Area Office Ph (09) 429 0044
Bookings essential all year

2732800E 6556200N
Hema Atlas Map Ref 36 D5

---

112 Map 12 C4

Akapoua Bay
Port Fitzroy DoC Headquarters, Great Barrier Island
(car ferry access)
DoC Great Barrier Island Area Office Ph (09) 429 0044
Bookings essential all year

2725300E 6555700N
Hema Atlas Map Ref 36 D4

---

113 Map 12 C4

Whangapoua
Edge of estuary at Okiwi, Great Barrier Island
(car ferry access)
DoC Great Barrier Island Area Office Ph (09) 429 0044
Bookings essential all year

2727900E 6560700N
Hema Atlas Map Ref 36 C4

SH1 — Auckland to Wellsford

114

Map 13 AB2

Auckland North Shore Top 10 Holiday Park
52 Northcote Rd, Glenfield: 500m W of SH1
Ph 0508 90 90 90 info@nsmotels.co.nz
Author's note — Nice camp and convenient location for access
to Kea Campers HQ.

2666000E 6488500N
Hema Atlas Ref 88 J4, 90 A4, 7 D4

115

Takapuna Beach Holiday Park

22 The Promenade, Takapuna: signposted from Hurstmere
Rd, at the N end of Takapuna town centre
Ph/Fax (09) 489 7909 takabeach@xtra.co.nz

Map 13 AB2

Author's note — Prime waterfront location, yet only a short stroll to the
cafes of Takapuna. Be warned, it can get a tad crowded.

2669400E 6489000N
Hema Atlas Ref 88 H5, 90 A4, 7 D4

116

Roadside Rest Area

Milford Beach Marina

Map 13 AB2

Author's note — Waterside picnic area.

2667500E 6491500N
Hema Atlas Map Ref 88 H4, 7 C4

117

Roadside Rest Area

Milford Beach Reserve

Map 13 AB2

Author's note — Waterside picnic area.

2668800E 6491600N
Hema Atlas Map Ref 88 H4, 7 C4

118

Roadside Rest Area

Castor Bay Beach Reserve

Map 13 AB2

Author's note — Waterside picnic area.

2668700E 6493000N
Hema Atlas Map Ref 88 G4, 7 C4

119

Roadside Rest Area

Mairangi Bay Beach Reserve

Map 13 AB2

Author's note — Waterside picnic area.

2667600E 6494900N
Hema Atlas Map Ref 88 G4, 7 C4

120

Roadside Rest Area

Browns Bay Beach Reserve: along the coastal route,
follow the signs to Browns Bay town centre

Map 13 AB2

Author's note — Waterside picnic area.

2667300E 6496800N
Hema Atlas Map Ref 88 F4, 7 C4

121

Shakespear Regional Park

Whangaparoa Peninsula: road's end, a 20km diversion
from the Hibiscus Coast route
Auckland Regional Council Ph (09) 366 2000
www.arc.govt.nz info@arc.govt.nz.

Map 13 AA3

Bookings essential all year

2672100E 6510000N
Hema Atlas Map Ref 88 B6, 7 B5

122

Pinewoods Holiday Park

23 Marie Ave, Red Beach: Follow the signs
to Red Beach from Hibiscus Highway
Ph (09) 426 4526 office@pinewoods.co.nz

Map 13 AA2

Author's note — Compact, sheltered and just a short walk
from the beach.

2663200E 6509500N
Hema Atlas Map Ref 88 B3, 7 B4

123 Orewa Beach Holiday Park

Map 13 AA2

265 Hibiscus Coast Highway: beachside at the
S end of Orewa Beach
Ph (09) 426 5832 obhpark@rodney.govt.nz

Author's note — Fabulous beachside location with a sheltered estuary
for safe swimming. Can get a tad crowded due to popularity.

2664400E 6510800N

Hema Atlas Map Ref 88 A3, 7 A4

124 Roadside Rest Area

Map 13 AA2

Moana Reserve: waterfront at Orewa

Author's note — Waterside picnic area.

2663200E 6510800N

Hema Atlas Map Ref 88 A3, 7 A4

125 Puriri Park Top 10 Holiday Resort

Map 13 AA2

290 Centreway Rd, Orewa: signposted
at N end of Orewa from SH1
Ph 0800 787 494 info@puriripark.com

Author's note — Set in 25 acres of bush, just 500m from Orewa Beach.

2660900E 6512500N

Hema Atlas Map Ref 88 A2, 7 A4

126 Roadside Rest Area

Map 13 AA2

Hatfields Beach, adjoining SH1

Author's note — Waterside picnic area.

2662800E 6513700N

Hema Atlas Map Ref 7 A4

127 Waiwera Holiday Park & Thermal Pools

Map 13 AA2

37 Waiwera Place, Waiwera: signposted from
SH1 at Waiwera
Ph (09) 426 5270 camp@waiwera.co.nz

Author's note — Compact camp, close to beach and hot pools.

2664000E 6515400N

Hema Atlas Map Ref 7 A4

128 Wenderholm Regional Park

Map 13 AA2

Alongside SH1 N of Hatfields Beach
Auckland Regional Council Ph (09) 366 2000
www.arc.govt.nz info@arc.govt.nz.

Bookings essential all year
Author's note — Features a lovely tree lined bay.

2664100E 6516600N

Hema Atlas Map Ref 7 A4

129 Mahurangi Regional Park

Map 12 D3

Signposted E of SH1, S of Warkworth
Auckland Regional Council Ph (09) 366 2000
www.arc.govt.nz info@arc.govt.nz

Bookings essential all year.
Author's note — Peaceful but simple camping.

2665000E 6520800N

Hema Atlas Map Ref 6 F10

130 Roadside Rest Area

Map 12 C3

Kowhai Park: N end of Warkworth on SH1

2660100E 6532100N

Hema Atlas Map Ref 6 E9

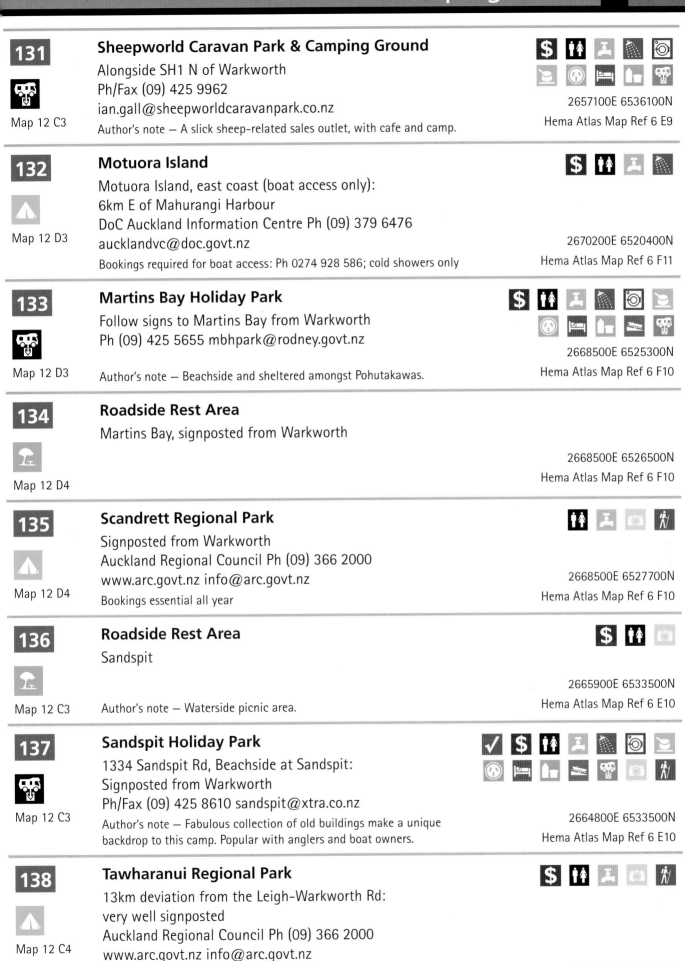

131

Map 12 C3

Sheepworld Caravan Park & Camping Ground
Alongside SH1 N of Warkworth
Ph/Fax (09) 425 9962
ian.gall@sheepworldcaravanpark.co.nz
Author's note — A slick sheep-related sales outlet, with cafe and camp.

2657100E 6536100N
Hema Atlas Map Ref 6 E9

132

Map 12 D3

Motuora Island
Motuora Island, east coast (boat access only):
6km E of Mahurangi Harbour
DoC Auckland Information Centre Ph (09) 379 6476
aucklandvc@doc.govt.nz
Bookings required for boat access: Ph 0274 928 586; cold showers only

2670200E 6520400N
Hema Atlas Map Ref 6 F11

133

Map 12 D3

Martins Bay Holiday Park
Follow signs to Martins Bay from Warkworth
Ph (09) 425 5655 mbhpark@rodney.govt.nz

Author's note — Beachside and sheltered amongst Pohutakawas.

2668500E 6525300N
Hema Atlas Map Ref 6 F10

134

Map 12 D4

Roadside Rest Area
Martins Bay, signposted from Warkworth

2668500E 6526500N
Hema Atlas Map Ref 6 F10

135

Map 12 D4

Scandrett Regional Park
Signposted from Warkworth
Auckland Regional Council Ph (09) 366 2000
www.arc.govt.nz info@arc.govt.nz
Bookings essential all year

2668500E 6527700N
Hema Atlas Map Ref 6 F10

136

Map 12 C3

Roadside Rest Area
Sandspit

Author's note — Waterside picnic area.

2665900E 6533500N
Hema Atlas Map Ref 6 E10

137

Map 12 C3

Sandspit Holiday Park
1334 Sandspit Rd, Beachside at Sandspit:
Signposted from Warkworth
Ph/Fax (09) 425 8610 sandspit@xtra.co.nz
Author's note — Fabulous collection of old buildings make a unique
backdrop to this camp. Popular with anglers and boat owners.

2664800E 6533500N
Hema Atlas Map Ref 6 E10

138

Map 12 C4

Tawharanui Regional Park
13km deviation from the Leigh-Warkworth Rd:
very well signposted
Auckland Regional Council Ph (09) 366 2000
www.arc.govt.nz info@arc.govt.nz
Bookings essential all year
Author's note — Beautiful camping and surfing beach with lots of walks.

2674300E 6533900N
Hema Atlas Map Ref 6 E11

139

Map 12 C3

Whangateau Holiday Park
559 Leigh Rd, Whangateau
Ph (09) 422 6305 whpark@rodney.govt.nz

Author's note — Waterside, but a bit exposed to sun and heat.

2669400E 6540900N
Hema Atlas Map Ref 6 D10

140

Map 12 C4

Goat Island Camping & Accommodation
A short deviation from the Leigh-Pakiri Rd: follow the signs
Ph (09) 422 6185 goatiscamp@xtra.co.nz

Author's note — If you are into fish watching rather than fish eating, then this funky camp provides a farm-like sheltered site overlooking the nearby Marine Reserve.

2672300E 6545700N
Hema Atlas Map Ref 6 D11

141

Map 12 C3

Roadside Rest Area
Okakari Point Scenic Reserve, Cape Rodney

Author's note — Popular point for access to nearby Marine Reserve. A glass-bottom boat operates from here, so bring your snorkel and flippers.

2671400E 6546800N
Hema Atlas Map Ref 6 D11

142

Map 12 C3

Pakiri Beach Holiday Park
261 Pakiri River Rd, Pakiri: follow signs to Pakiri
from either Wellsford or Leigh
Ph/Fax (09) 422 6199 pakiri@khh.co.nz

Author's note — Extremely well-managed beachside camp with great facilities. Rare five star Qualmark rating.

2665500E 6549600N
Hema Atlas Map Ref 6 D10

SH16 — Wellsford to Auckland

143

Map 12 C3

Roadside Rest Area
Alongside SH16: scenic lookout 208m above sea level

2641900E 6538400N
Hema Atlas Map Ref 6 E8

144

Map 12 C3

Roadside Rest Area
Omeru Reserve, alongside SH16

2640900E 6533200N
Hema Atlas Map Ref 6 E8

145

Map 13 AA1

Roadside Rest Area
Alongside SH16

2643700E 6513900N
Hema Atlas Map Ref 6 G8

146

Map 13 AA1

Aquatic Park & Motor Camp
Parkhurst Rd, Parakai
Ph (09) 420 8998 aquaticpark@xtra.co.nz

Author's note — Located next to a major thermal pool complex for swimming and soothing those aches. A simple camp equivalent to a 2-3 star rating.

2639200E 6504000N
Hema Atlas Map Ref 5 H7

147

Roadside Rest Area

Shelly Beach Rd, Helensville

Map 12 D3   Author's note — Waterside picnic area.

2633100E 6514400N

Hema Atlas Map Ref 5 G7

148

Shelly Beach Camping Ground

Shelly Beach Rd, Helensville

Ph (09) 420 2595 www.rodney.govt.nz

Swimming, fishing

Map 12 D3   Author's note — Harbourside location with a white shell beach.

2634300E 6514400N

Hema Atlas Map Ref 5 G7

149

Muriwai Beach Motor Camp

Beachfront at Murawai

Ph (09) 411 9262

Surfing, angling. Author's note — Sheltered tree-clad site right
next to this rugged West Coast beach.

Map 13 AB1

2637500E 6486000N

Hema Atlas Map Ref 7 D1

150

Glen Esk Road

Waitakere Regional Park

Auckland Regional Council Ph (09) 366 2000

www.arc.govt.nz info@arc.govt.nz

Map 13 AC1   Bookings essential all year

2643500E 6471500N

Hema Atlas Map Ref 7 E2

151

Piha Domain Motor Camp

21 Seaview Rd, Piha

Ph/Fax (09) 812 8815 pihacamp@xtra.co.nz

Surfing, angling Author's note — Pretty beachside spot with
no Cabins, but some caravans available.

Map 13 AC1

2642300E 6471300N

Hema Atlas Map Ref 7 E2

152

Roadside Rest Area

S of Piha

Map 13 AC1

2640800E 6469800N

Hema Atlas Map Ref 7 F2

153

Log Jam Road

Waitakere Regional Park

Auckland Regional Council Ph (09) 366 2000 www.arc.govt.

nz info@arc.govt.nz

Map 13 AC1   Bookings essential all year

2641400E 6468600N

Hema Atlas Map Ref 7 F2

Auckland to Waitakere Regional Park

154

Roadside Rest Area

Waikowhai Park: alongside Route 15, SW of Auckland

Map 13 AC2

2663200E 6473200N

Hema Atlas Map Ref 89 D3, 7 E4

155

Map 13 AC2

Avondale Motor Park

46 Bollard Ave, Avondale: signposted from
New North Rd, S of Mt Albert township
Ph 0800 100 542 avondalemotorpark@xtra.co.nz

Author's note — Clean and compact site that makes a good base
for entering/leaving Auckland from the West and exploring areas
such as Titirangi, Piha and Murawai.

2662800E 6476600N
Hema Atlas Map Ref 89 C3, 7 E4

156

Map 13 AC2

Roadside Rest Area

Craigavon Park: alongside Route 15, SW Auckland

2661000E 6474600N
Hema Atlas Map Ref 89 D3, 7 E4

157

Map 13 AC2

Roadside Rest Area

Rahui Kahika Reserve: alongside Route 15, Titirangi

2659100E 6473800N
Hema Atlas Map Ref 89 D2, 7 E3

158

Map 13 AC2

Roadside Rest Area

Huia Rd, Titirangi

2656100E 6471900N
Hema Atlas Map Ref 89 D2, 7 E3

159

Map 13 AC1

Arataki Visitors Centre

Waitakere Regional Park: alongside Scenic Route 24
between Titirangi & Waiatarua
Auckland Regional Council Ph (09) 366 2000
www.arc.govt.nz info@arc.govt.nz

Bookings essential all year; overnight for campervans allowed

2653000E 6472700N
Hema Atlas Map Ref 89 D2, 7 E3

160

Map 13 AC2

Roadside Rest Area

Huia Rd, Mill Bay, Waitakere Regional Park

Author's note — Several picnic spots in this vicinity.

2653800E 6466300N
Hema Atlas Map Ref 89 E2, 7 F3

161

Map 13 AC1

Roadside Rest Area

Beachfront along Huia Rd, Huia Bay,
Waitakere Regional Park

2650500E 6466600N
Hema Atlas Map Ref 89 E1, 7 F3

162

Map 13 AC1

Karamatura Farm Camp

Huia Rd, 2km past Huia Bay, Waitakere Regional Park
Auckland Regional Council Ph (09) 366 2000
www.arc.govt.nz info@arc.govt.nz

Bookings essential all year. Author's note — Simple camping in a rural
environment, handy to the Manukau Harbour.

2648600E 6465300N
Hema Atlas Map Ref 89 E1, 7 F2

Auckland to SH25

163 Roadside Rest Area
Okahu Bay Reserve, Tamaki Drive

Map 13 AB3 Author's note — Waterside picnic area.

2671700E 6482400N
Hema Atlas Map Ref 90 C5, 7 D5

164 Roadside Rest Area
Mission Bay, Tamaki Drive

Author's note — Waterside picnic area with iconic views of Rangitoto Island.

Map 13 AB3

2673400E 6483100N
Hema Atlas Map Ref 90 B5, 7 D5

165 Remuera Motor Lodge
16 Minto Rd, Remuera: signposted SW of Remuera Rd,
S of Remuera township
Ph 0508 244 244 remlodge@ihug.co.nz

Map 13 AC3 Author's note — Small, compact site in a suprisingly quiet wooded valley only a stone's throw from the cafes of Remuera Rd.

2672300E 6478000N
Hema Atlas Map Ref 90 C5, 7 E5

166 Omana Regional Park
Signposted near Beachlands on the Whitford to Clevedon coastal road (Whitford Maraetai Coast Road)
Auckland Regional Council Ph (09) 366 2000
www.arc.govt.nz info@arc.govt.nz

Map 12 D4

Bookings essential all year

2690400E 6478700N
Hema Atlas Map Ref 7 E7

167 Maraetai Beach Reserve
Alongside Whitford to Clevedon coastal road

2692900E 6478700N
Hema Atlas Map Ref 7 E7

Map 12 D4

168 Duder Regional Park
Alongside Whitford to Clevedon coastal road
Auckland Regional Council Ph (09) 366 2000
www.arc.govt.nz info@arc.govt.nz

Map 12 D4 Bookings essential all year

2695400E 6474500N
Hema Atlas Map Ref 7 E7

169 Roadside Rest Area
Kawakawa Bay, on the Clevedon to Kaiaua road

2702900E 6470900N
Hema Atlas Map Ref 8 E8

Map 12 D4 Author's note — Waterside picnic area.

170 Orere Point Top 10 Holiday Park
2 Orere Point Rd, Orere Point: on the
Clevedon to Kaiaua road
Ph 0800 391 905 orerepoint@xtra.co.nz

Map 12 D4 Boating, fishing
Author's note — Pretty location, just back from the beach.

2710400E 6468400N
Hema Atlas Map Ref 8 F9

171

Roadside Rest Area

Orere Point on the Clevedon to Kaiaua road

Map 12 D4   Author's note — Waterside picnic area.

2710400E 6469600N
Hema Atlas Map Ref 8 F9

172

Tapapakanga Regional Park

On the Clevedon to Miranda Coast road
Auckland Regional Council Ph (09) 366 2000
www.arc.govt.nz info@arc.govt.nz
Bookings essential all year

Map 12 D4

2711400E 6467000N
Hema Atlas Map Ref 8 F9

173

Waharau Regional Park

On the Clevedon to Miranda Coast road
Auckland Regional Council Ph (09) 366 2000
www.arc.govt.nz info@arc.govt.nz
Bookings essential all year

Map 12 D4

2714900E 6460900N
Hema Atlas Map Ref 8 F9

174

Roadside Rest Area

On the Clevedon to Miranda Coast road

Map 12 D4   Author's note — Waterside picnic area.

2715400E 6459800N
Hema Atlas Map Ref 8 G9

175

Kaiaua Motor Camp

Coast Road, Kaiaua
Ph (09) 232 2879 Fax (09) 232 2821
camp@ecoquest.co.nz

Map 12 D4

2713800E 6452800N
Hema Atlas Map Ref 8 G9

176

Upper Mangatawhiri Camp Ground

Hunua Range Regional Park
Auckland Regional Council Ph (09) 366 2000
www.arc.govt.nz info@arc.govt.nz
Bookings essential all year

Map 12 D4

2701000E 6454800N
Hema Atlas Map Ref 8 G8

177

Rays Rest Roadside Reserve

On the Clevedon to Miranda Coast road

Author's note — Little more than a paddock, but 'free camping'
seems to occur here.

Map 12 E4

2714500E 6447100N
Hema Atlas Map Ref 8 H9

178

Miranda Holiday Park

On the Clevedon to Miranda Coast road
Ph (07) 867 3205

Map 12 E4   Author's note — Right next to the Miranda Hot Thermal Pools.

2717400E 6440400N
Hema Atlas Map Ref 8 H9

SH1 — Auckland to SH2

179

Map 13 AC2

Ambury Regional Park

Ambury Rd, Manukau: follow SH20 taking the Mangere Bridge offramp, Ambury Park is signposted from here
Auckland Regional Council Ph (09) 366 2000
www.arc.govt.nz info@arc.govt.nz

Bookings essential all year
Author's note — Simple camping in a picturesque rural location, yet only 30 min from downtown Auckland, and 15 min from the airport.

2667400E 6471700N
Hema Atlas Map Ref 90 D4, 7 E4

180

Map 13 AC3

Manukau Top 10 Holiday Park

902 Great South Rd, Manukau: take the Manukau exit from SH1, head S on Great Sth Rd from Manukau city centre and Rainbow's End
Ph 0800 422 6737 info@manukautop10.co.nz

Author's note — A suprisingly peaceful, small camp handy to S Auckland and Manukau City Centre. An ideal base for campers returning their hire vehicles to the nearby Auckland airport.

2678300E 6464300N
Hema Atlas Map Ref 90 E5, 7 F5

181

Map 12 E4

South Auckland Caravan Park

47 Ararimu Rd, Ramarama: signposted from the Ramarama exit SH1, S of Auckland
Ph (09) 294 8903 sacp@xtra.co.nz

2683900E 6449800N
Hema Atlas Map Ref 7 H6

Author's note — A rural setting, handy to South Auckland.

182

Map 12 E3

Clarks Beach Holiday Park

Torkar Rd, Clarks Beach: signposted from the town centre at Clarks Beach, exit SH1 at Papakura, and follow signs to Kingseat and Waiau Pa
Ph (09) 232 1685 cbhp@ihug.co.nz

Author's note — Opposite a tree-lined waterside recreational area, with boat launching and picnicking facilities. Also handy to a golf course. It's a little hard to find, but a nice spot south of Auckland.

2660300E 6449700N
Hema Atlas Map Ref 7 H4

183

Map 12 D3

Roadside Rest Area

Torkar Rd, Clarks Beach: signposted from the town centre at Clarks Beach, exit SH1 at Papakura, and follow signs to Kingseat and Waiau Pa

Author' note — Waterside picnic area.

2659900E 6450900N
Hema Atlas Map Ref 7 G4

184

Map 12 E3

Sandspit Motor Camp

15 Rangiwhea Rd, Waiuku: signposted N of Waiuku town centre
Ph/Fax (09) 235 9913 sandspitmotor@xtra.co.nz

Author's note — This has a nice location, next to a waterfront reserve, but it is perhaps more suited to permanents. Casuals choice could be Clarks Beach 30 min away.

2663500E 6439800N
Hema Atlas Map Ref 7 J4

185

Map 12 D3

Awhitu

Awhitu Regional Park
Auckland Regional Council (09) 366 2000
www.arc.govt.nz infor@arc.govt.nz
Bookings essential all year

2656900E 6455600N
Hema Atlas Map Ref 7 G3

186

Map 12 D3

Big Bay Motor Camp & Fishing Lodge

271 Big Bay Rd, Awhitu: follow signs to Manukau Heads
from Waiuku then to Big Bay
Ph (09) 235 1132

Author's note — Simple and compact site, only 100m from
a pretty beach.

2655500E 6460900N
Hema Atlas Map Ref 7 F3

187

Map 12 D3

Orua Bay Beach Motor Camp

294 Orua Bay Rd: signposted from Awhitu, 30 min N of
Waiuku, follow signs to Manukau Heads, then to Awhitu,
Orua Bay is signposted from there
Ph (09) 235 1129 oruabay@ihug.co.nz

Author's note — A clean and quiet camp in a magic location,
I'm amazed that more Aucklanders have not discovered this spot,
less than two hours from Auckland (depending on the traffic!).

2653600E 6460700N
Hema Atlas Map Ref 7 F3

CENTRAL NORTH REGION

Craters of the Moon

SH1 — From SH2 to Hamilton

188

Map 12 E4

Roadside Rest Area

Les Batton Reserve, Port Waikato Rd, W of Tauranganui:
beside the Waikato River

Author's note — Riverside swimming and boating opportunities.

2683600E 6432300N
Hema Atlas Map Ref 9 D3

189

Map 12 E3

Port Waikato Holiday Park

115 Maunsell Rd, Port Waikato
Ph (09) 232 9857 info@portwaikatoholidaypark.co.nz

Author's note — Laidback little community with old-style Kiwi batches.

2662500E 6422800N
Hema Atlas Map Ref 9 E1

190

Map 12 E4

**Waingaro Hot Springs Caravan Park
& Hot Pools**

Alongside Waingaro Rd, at Waingaro
Ph/Fax (07) 825 4761 waingaro.hotsprings@clear.net.nz

Author's note — A peaceful rural location — a great place to unwind.

2686100E 6388900N
Hema Atlas Map Ref 9 J3

191

Map 12 E3

Raglan Kopua Holiday Park

Marine Parade, Raglan: well signposted from the town
centre, just off the road to the surf beaches
Ph (07) 825 8283 raglanholidaypark@xtra.co.nz

Author's note — A huge camp beside the estuary for boating and swimming, yet just a short walk across a bridge to the town centre.

2673300E 6376200N
Hema Atlas Map Ref 11 C3

192

Map 12 E3

Wainui Beach Reserve

Off Wainui Rd, S of Raglan

Author's note — Access point to the great Raglan surf beach.

2671300E 6374900N
Hema Atlas Map Ref 11 C3

193

Map 12 E3

Solscape

Follow Wainui Rd S from Raglan towards Manu Bay:
roadside on the way to Whale Bay
Ph (07) 825 8268 www.solscape.co.nz

Author's note — A small peaceful location on a hill overlooking the
famous Raglan surf break.

2669300E 6373200N
Hema Atlas Map Ref 11 C2

194

Map 12 E4

Hamilton City Holiday Park

14 Ruakura Rd, Claudelands: from Hamilton Centre
cross the Claudelands Bridge and follow signs to the
Waikato University
Ph (07) 855 8255 hchp@xtra.co.nz

Author's note — Close to the city centre, in spacious park-like grounds.

2712200E 6377900N
Hema Atlas Map Ref 92 E4, 11 C7

195

Map 12 E4

Hamilton East Motor Camp

61 Cameron Rd, Hamilton East
Ph/Fax (07) 856 6220 tourist.court@clear.net.nz

2713400E 6377300N
Hema Atlas Map Ref 92 F5, 11 C7

SH3 — Hamilton to Te Kuiti

196
Map 14 A4

Roadrunner Motel and Holiday Park
141 Bond Rd, Te Awamutu
Ph (07) 871 7420 Fax (07) 871 6664 road.runner@xtra.co.nz

2715300E 6353800N
Hema Atlas Map Ref 11 E7

197
Map 14 B4

Roadside Rest Area
Alongside SH3

2713800E 6340500N
Hema Atlas Map Ref 11 F7

198
Map 14 B4

Otorohanga Holiday Park
12 Huiputea Drive, Otorohanga: signposted at
N end of Otorohanga
Ph (07) 873 7253 bill@kiwiholidaypark.co.nz
Author's note — Impressive and relatively new facilities,
including a fitness centre.

2704700E 6332400N
Hema Atlas Map Ref 11 G6

199
Map 14 B4

Kiwitown Holiday Park
Domain Drive, Otorohanga: follow signs to the Kiwi House

Casual Camping — a caretaker may collect koha or fees if they are in
attendance. Author's note — Compact, neat and tidy.

2703600E 6334200N
Hema Atlas Map Ref 11 G6

200
Map 14 A4

Roadside Rest Area
Alongside SH31

2683400E 6347400N
Hema Atlas Map Ref 11 F4

201
Map 14 A4

Kawhia Beachside S-Cape
225 Pouewe St, Kawhia: signposted alongside
the main road at the entrance to Kawhia
PH (07) 871 0727 kawhiabeachsidescape@xtra.co.nz
Boating, angling

2671200E 6348300N
Hema Atlas Map Ref 11 F3

202
Map 14 A4

Forest View Motor Camp
232 Waiwera St, Kawhia: follow signs to the
boat ramp from the town centre
Ph/Fax (07) 871 0858
Boating, angling

2669500E 6348400N
Hema Atlas Map Ref 11 F2

203
Map 14 A4

Kawhia Camping Ground
73 Moko St, Kawhia: follow signs to the boat ramp from the
town centre
Ph (07) 871 0863 dinic@xtra.co.nz
Boating, angling

2669200E 6347200N
Hema Atlas Map Ref 11 F2

204

Map 14 B4

Roadside Rest Area

Alongside SH2 S of Otorohanga

2701000E 6328400N
Hema Atlas Map Ref 11 H6

205

Map 14 B4

Waitomo Top 10 Holiday Park

Follow the signs to Waitomo Caves from SH3: campsite
is almost opposite Waitomo's Information Centre and
Caves Museum, 800m from Waitomo Caves
Ph 0508 498 666 stay@waitomopark.co.nz

Author's note – Small, compact, neat and tidy as well as very
convenient location.

2694100E 6325900N
Hema Atlas Map Ref 11 H5

206

Map 14 B4

Te Kuiti Domain Camping Ground

Domain Access Rd, Te Kuiti: follow signs to the
Town Centre, camp signposted at the N end of town

Casual Camping – a caretaker may collect koha or fees if they are in
attendance. Author's note – All the facilities you need, in a compact,
sheltered and cosy camp adjoining a domain reserve.

2699600E 6317700N
Hema Atlas Map Ref 11 J5

207

Map 14 B4

Roadside Rest Area

Overlooking Te Kuiti from SH3 S of the township

2701600E 6315400N
Hema Atlas Map Ref 11 J6

SH3 — Te Kuiti to New Plymouth

208

Map 14 B4

Roadside Rest Area

Alongside SH3 at the N end of Piopio

2686300E 6303200N
Hema Atlas Map Ref 18 A8

209

Map 14 B4

Roadside Rest Area

Alongside SH3 at Paemako Scenic Reserve

2679200E 6299700N
Hema Atlas Map Ref 17 B7

210

Map 14 B4

Seaview Holiday Park

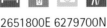

Alongside SH3 at Sunset Beach, N of Mokau
Ph/Fax (06) 752 9708 seaview.holidaypark@xtra.co.nz

Author's note – Compact, neat and tidy site on an interesting
stretch of coast.

2651800E 6279700N
Hema Atlas Map Ref 17 D5

211

Map 14 B3

Roadside Rest Area

Alongside SH3 and the Mohakatino River

2650000E 6278100N
Hema Atlas Map Ref 17 D5

212

Map 14 B3

Whitebait Inn Cabins & Motor Camp
Alongside SH3 in the centre of Mokau
Enquiries to the Whitebait Inn Ph (06) 752 9713
Author's note — Compact, and close to the town centre with access to nearby river and beaches.

2649800E 6276900N
Hema Atlas Map Ref 17 D5

213

Map 14 B3

Roadside Rest Area
Beachside SH3, S of Mokau

2648700E 6270900N
Hema Atlas Map Ref 17 D4

214

Map 14 C3

Roadside Rest Area
Alongside SH3 at the Rapuni Stream bridge

2647600E 6266400N
Hema Atlas Map Ref 17 E4

215

Map 14 C3

Roadside Rest Area
Alongside SH3 at Tongaporutu

2649100E 6265100N
Hema Atlas Map Ref 17 E4

216

Map 14 C3

Roadside Rest Area
Three Sisters Reserve: a 800m deviation from SH3 at the S end of Tongaporutu bridge

2647500E 6263500N
Hema Atlas Map Ref 17 E4

217

Map 14 C3

Roadside Rest Area
Alongside SH3 at the summit of Mt Messenger (192m)

2647300E 6255700N
Hema Atlas Map Ref 17 F4

218

Map 14 C3

Roadside Rest Area
Beachside at Wai-iti Beach: a 4km deviation from SH3

2637200E 6252500N
Hema Atlas Map Ref 17 F3

219

Map 14 C3

Urenui Beach Camp Ground
148 Beach Rd, Urenui: a 2km deviation
signposted from SH3 at Urenui
Ph/Fax (06) 752 3838 urenuibeachcamp@xtra.co.nz
Author's note — A large camp that's handy to both a nearby beach and estuary and adjoining a golf course.

2630300E 6245400N
Hema Atlas Map Ref 17 G3

220
Map 14 C3

Onaero Bay Holiday Park

Beachside, a short diversion from SH3 at Onaero
Ph (06) 752 3643 nzmca.onaero@xtra.co.nz
Author's note – Nice location, managed by the NZ Motor
Caravan Association.

2628900E 6245200N
Hema Atlas Map Ref 17 G2

221
Map 14 C3

Roadside Rest Area

Waitara Marine Park, Waitara

2614700E 6246000N
Hema Atlas Map Ref 17 G1

222
Map 14 C3

Marine Park Motor Park

Centennial Ave, Waitara: follow signs from
Waitara town centre to Beach Reserve & Domain
Ph (06) 754 7121
Author's note – Huge park-like grounds next to the beach
and a favoured rivermouth fishing spot.

2615900E 6246000N
Hema Atlas Map Ref 17 G1

223
Map 14 C3

Sentry Hill Motel & Roadhouse

56 Mountain Rd, New Plymouth: N end of SH3A
New Plymouth bypass
Ph 0800 74 84 733 www.sentryhill.co.nz
Author's note – There is no provision for tent camping so
the site is only suitable for caravans, RVs and campervans.

2613000E 6240600N
Hema Atlas Map Ref 23 A6

224
Map 14 C3

Fitzroy Beach Holiday Park

Beach St, Fitzroy: signposted N of SH3,
E of New Plymouth at Fitzroy
Ph/Fax (06) 758 2870 fitzroybeach@xtra.co.nz
Author's note – Right on the beach at a favoured surf spot
and linked to the city centre by the fabulous coastal walkway.

2605500E 6239500N
Hema Atlas Map Ref 107 A5, 23 B5

225
Map 14 C3

New Plymouth Top 10 Holiday Park

29 Princes St, Fitzroy: signposted N of SH3
E of New Plymouth
Ph 0800 758 256 new.plymouth.topten@xtra.co.nz
Author's note – Sheltered, clean and tidy site just a 500m
walk to the beach.

2605500E 6239500N
Hema Atlas Map Ref 107 A5, 23 B5

SH4 — Te Kuiti to Ohakune

226
Map 14 C4

Taumarunui Holiday Park & Roadside Rest Area

SH4, South Taumarunui: 3km S of Taumarunui
Ph 0800 473 281 www.taumarunuiholidaypark.co.nz
Author's note – Neat and tidy in a nice sheltered setting.
Train spotters will enjoy the location.

2710900E 6255900N
Hema Atlas Map Ref 18 F11

227

🏕️ Map 14 C4

Roadside Rest Area

Ohinetonga Scenic Reserve, off SH4
DoC Ohakune Visitor Centre Ph (06) 385 0010
ohakunevc@doc.govt.nz

2716900E 6243000N
Hema Atlas Map Ref 18 G11

228

🏕️ Map 14 C4

Whakahoro

End of Oio Rd, off SH4 at Owhango
DoC Whanganui Area Office Ph (06) 348 8475

Fee applies for using facilities at Whakahoro Hut

2690400E 6232500N
Hema Atlas Map Ref 18 H9

229

🏕️ Map 14 C4

Mangahuia

Off SH47: 6km from National Park township
DoC Ohakune Visitor Centre Ph (06) 385 0010
ohakunevc@doc.govt.nz

Self registration system.
Author's note — Handy for a great variety of walks and sightseeing.

2724200E 6221600N
Hema Atlas Map Ref 18 J12

230

🏕️ Map 14 C4

Discovery Lodge

Along SH47: 1km S of junction of SH47 & SH48
Ph 0800 122 122 info@discovery.net.nz

Author's note — Good location and looks great, but best treated
as 2-3 star camping.

2724100E 6224200N
Hema Atlas Map Ref 18 J12

231

🚐 Map 15 C5

Whakapapa Motor Camp

SH48 adjacent Whakapapa Visitor Centre,
Whakapapa Village, Tongariro National Park
DoC Whakapapa Visitor Centre Ph (07) 892 3729
whakapapavc@doc.govt.nz; Bookings Ph (07) 892 3897
whakapapaholpark@xtra.co.nz

Author's note — Compact, sheltered and handy to Whakapapa Village
with skiing and walking opportunities as the seasons allow.

2726900E 6219500N
Hema Atlas Map Ref 18 J13

232

🌳 Map 14 C4

Roadside Rest Area

Adjacent SH4, S of National Park

2717000E 6213800N
Hema Atlas Map Ref 26 A11

233

🌳 Map 14 C4

Roadside Rest Area

Adjacent SH4, S of National Park

2716900E 6211700N
Hema Atlas Map Ref 26 A11

234

🚐 Map 14 C4

Ohakune Top 10 Holiday Park

5 Moore St, Ohakune: signposted S of SH49,
W side of village
Ph (06) 385 8561 www.ohakune.net.nz
Author's note — Neat and tidy site right next to a bush reserve.

2715500E 6196000N
Hema Atlas Map Ref 26 C11

235

Map 14 C4

Mangawhero

Ohakune Mountain Rd: 2km from Ohakune
DoC Ohakune Visitor Centre Ph (06) 385 0010
ohakunevc@doc.govt.nz

Self registration system.
Author's note — Handy to a wide range of mountain activities.

2718000E 6198500N
Hema Atlas Map Ref 26 C11

SH1 — Waiouru to Taupo

236

Map 15 C5

Roadside Rest Area

Adjacent SH49 W of Waiouru, at the Tangiwai
Disaster Memorial

2731000E 6190600N
Hema Atlas Map Ref 26 C13

237

Map 15 C5

Roadside Rest Area

Alongside SH1 (Desert Rd): summit is 1077m above
sea level

2745200E 6207400N
Hema Atlas Map Ref 26 B14

238

Map 15 C5

Roadside Rest Area

W of SH1 (Desert Rd): beside Oturere Stream

2747700E 6221400N
Hema Atlas Map Ref 19 J2

239

Map 15 C5

Tonagariro Holiday Park

Near junction of SH47 and SH46, S of Turangi
Ph (07) 386 8062 www.thp.co.nz

Author's note — Adequate site with good cabins for skiing
and camping bases.

2735400E 6237400N
Hema Atlas Map Ref 19 H1

240

Map 15 C5

Lake View Rest Area

Adjacent SH47

2748500E 6243000N
Hema Atlas Map Ref 19 G2

241

Map 15 C5

Oasis Motel & Holiday Park

SH41 at Tokaanu
Ph (07) 386 8569 oasismotelstokaanu@xtra.co.nz

2749400E 6244100N
Hema Atlas Map Ref 19 G2

242

Map 15 C5

Roadside Rest Area

100m off SH41, W of Tokaanu

2746500E 6246400N
Hema Atlas Map Ref 19 G2

243

Map 15 C5

Habitat Motels

25 Ohuanga Rd, Turangi
Ph (07) 386 7492 clubhabitat@xtra.co.nz

2752900E 6242800N
Hema Atlas Map Ref 19 G3

244

Map 15 C5

Best Western Parklands Motor Lodge

Cnr SH1 & Arahori St, Turangi: opposite the
Shell petrol station
Ph 0800 456 284
Author's note — A handy trout fishing base.

2752900E 6242800N
Hema Atlas Map Ref 19 G3

245

Map 15 C5

Turangi Cabins & Holiday Park

Ohuanga Rd, Turangi
Ph/Fax (07) 386 8754 cabinsgalore@xtra.co.nz
Author's note — I liked this former single man's work camp:
it's my choice of a budget base in Turangi.

2752900E 6242800N
Hema Atlas Map Ref 19 G3

246

Map 15 C5

Rest Area

Adjoining SH1 at Turangi: N end of township, by the river

2754100E 6243400N
Hema Atlas Map Ref 19 G3

247

Map 15 C5

Motuoapa Motor Camp

13 Parekarangaranga St, Motuoapa: signposted from SH1
Ph/Fax (07) 386 7162 motuoapamotorcamp@xtra.co.nz
Author's note — Lakeside, but it can get crowded and there is not
a lot of shade.

2758600E 6249000N
Hema Atlas Map Ref 19 G3

248

Map 15 C5

Roadside Rest Area

Lakeside adjacent to SH1 and Lake Taupo

2765300E 6253100N
Hema Atlas Map Ref 19 F4

249

Map 15 C5

Motutere Bay Holiday Park

Lakeside at Motutere: adjacent to SH1 and Lake Taupo
Ph/Fax (07) 386 8963
Author's note — Hard to get a better lakeside spot: plenty of shade,
good swimming, boating and fishing.

2766400E 6253900N
Hema Atlas Map Ref 19 F4

250

Map 15 C5

Waipehu Reserve & Picnic Area

Lakeside adjacent to SH1 and Lake Taupo

2767600E 6254500N
Hema Atlas Map Ref 19 F4

251

Map 15 C5

Halletts Bay Picnic Area

Lakeside adjacent to SH1 and Lake Taupo

2770300E 6255700N
Hema Atlas Map Ref 19 F5

252

Map 15 C5

Windsor Lodge Motel & Caravan Park

Lakeside at Waitahanui: adjacent to SH1 and Lake Taupo

Ph (07) 378 6271 windsor.lodge@xtra.co.nz

Author's note — A favoured trout fishing spot.

2776600E 6264000N

Hema Atlas Map Ref 19 E5

253

Map 15 C5

Lakeside Rest Area

Lakeside at Waitahanui: adjacent to SH1 and Lake Taupo

2776700E 6265500N

Hema Atlas Map Ref 19 E5

254

Map 15 B5

5 Mile Bay Rest Area

Lakeside adjacent to SH1 and Lake Taupo

2776300E 6268800N

Hema Atlas Map Ref 98 D4, 19 E5

255

Map 15 B5

De Bretts Thermal Resort

Napier Taupo Hwy (SH5): from SH1 follow Lake Terrace
for 2.5km then turn onto SH5 for 1km

Ph (07) 378 8559 www.debrettsresort.co.nz

info@debrettsresort.co.nz

Author's note — Well-established grounds with a long
and proud tradition as a spa resort.

2779300E 6274000N

Hema Atlas Map Ref 98 B5, 19 D5

256

Map 15 B5

Taupo All Seasons Holiday Park

16 Rangatira St, Taupo: signposted from Spa Rd

Ph 0800 777 272 reservations@allseasons.nzl.com

2778200E 6275000N

Hema Atlas Map Ref 98 B4 19 D5

257

Map 15 B5

Great Lake Holiday Park

406 Acacia Bay Rd, Taupo: signposted from SH5 N of Taupo

Ph (07) 378 5159 atlake@xtra.co.nz

2774600E 6275500N

Hema Atlas Map Ref 98 B3, 19 D5

258

Map 15 B5

Lake Taupo Top 10 Holiday Resort

28 Centennial Drive, Taupo: signposted off Spa Rd

Ph 0800 332 121 office@taupotop10.co.nz

Author's note — New facilities and rated five star. It has all the trim-
mings, and the Taupo Aquatic Centre just a short walk away.

2779200E 6276900N

Hema Atlas Map Ref 98 A5, 19 D5

SH2 — SH1 to Tauranga

259

Map 12 E4

Roadside Rest Area

N side of SH2 E of Maramarua

2713600E 6434300N

Hema Atlas Map Ref 9 D6

260

Roadside Rest Area

Along SH26 S of Paeroa

Map 13 E5

2749100E 6407800N

Hema Atlas Map Ref 10 G9

261

Te Aroha Holiday Park

217 Stanley Rd, Te Aroha: signposted 3km SW
of Te Aroha on SH 26
Ph/Fax (07) 884 9567 oaktree@clear.net.nz

Author's note — Sheltered park-like grounds make this site
a good base from which to explore the hot pools.

Map 13 E5

2750700E 6400600N

Hema Atlas Map Ref 10 G10

262

Roadside Rest Area

SH26: NE of Morrinsville

Map 12 E4

2743200E 6398500N

Hema Atlas Map Ref 10 H9

263

Roadside Rest Area

SH27: NW of Matamata or W of Morrinsville

Map 12 E4

2744200E 6391900N

Hema Atlas Map Ref 10 H9

264

Dickey Flat

At the end of Dickey Flat Rd, Kaimai-Mamaku Conservation
Park: 10km SW of Waihi, off SH2
DoC www.doc.govt.nz or Tourism Rotorua Ph (07) 348 5170
tourism.rotorua@rdc.govt.nz

Drinking water is from a stream

Map 13 E5

2753700E 6414600N

Hema Atlas Map Ref 10 F10

265

Waihi Motor Camp

6 Waitete Rd, Waihi: signposted on SH2 W of the town
Ph (07) 863 7654

Author's note — A sheltered little valley, not too far from the
town, or gold mine.

Map 13 E5

2760000E 6419900N

Hema Atlas Map Ref 10 F10

266

Roadside Rest Area

On the outskirts of Waihi

Map 13 E5

2761300E 6420100N

Hema Atlas Map Ref 10 F11

267

Beach Haven Motel & Holiday Camp

21 Leo St, Waihi Beach: follow signs
to Waihi Beach from SH2
Ph/Fax (07) 863 5505

Author's note — This has the appearance more of a motel than
a campground but it is useful if needed.

Map 13 E5

2771000E 6418100N

Hema Atlas Map Ref 10 F12

268

Map 13 E5

Waihi Beach Top 10

15 Beach Rd, Waihi Beach: follow signs
to Waihi Beach from SH2
Ph 0800 924 448 info@waihibeach.com

Author's note — A great location: nestled into the bush, yet right in the
heart of the 'old town' and right on the beach.

2770200E 6416400N
Hema Atlas Map Ref 10 F12

269

Map 13 E5

Sea Air Motels & Holiday Park

Emerton Rd, off Waihi Beach Rd: follow signs to Waihi
Beach from SH2
Ph (07) 863 5655 sea-air@paradise.net.nz

Author's note — More a motel than a campground.

2771100E 6415000N
Hema Atlas Map Ref 10 F12

270

Map 13 E5

Athenree Hot Springs & Holiday Park

Athenree Rd, Athenree: 4km NE of SH2
Ph/Fax (07) 863 5600 hotsprings@xtra.co.nz

Author's note — Across the road from a sheltered estuary.
Fishing and boating options abound from this award-winning
and friendly little camp.

2772600E 6412200N
Hema Atlas Map Ref 10 F12

271

Map 13 E5

Bowentown Beach Holiday Park

Seaforth Rd, Bowentown: S of Waihi Beach and NE of SH2
Ph/Fax (07) 863 5381 bowentownhp@netsmart.net.nz

Author's note — This little paradise has been 'discovered'
and is rapidly changing. It's well worth the deviation from
SH2 to check out this delight.

2773600E 6411100N
Hema Atlas Map Ref 10 F12

272

Map 13 E5

Beachfront Reserve Picnic Area

Bowentown: S of Waihi Beach and NE of SH2

Author's note — Well worth a picnic here if you decide not to stay at
the nearby Bowentown Holiday Park.

2774800E 6410400N
Hema Atlas Map Ref 10 F12

273

Map 13 E5

Athenree Lavender Holiday Park

Adjacent SH2: about 13km S of Waihi in the Athenree
Forest Gorge
Ph/Fax (07) 549 4812 athenreelavender@paradise.net.nz

Author's note — Sheltered spot handy to stream with nice
swimming holes.

2768500E 6412400N
Hema Atlas Map Ref 10 F11

274

Map 13 E5

Roadside Rest Area

Adjacent SH2: E of turnoff to Athenree

2770600E 6411400N
Hema Atlas Map Ref 10 F12

275

Map 13 E5

Roadside Rest Area

Adjacent SH2: E of Katikati

2767100E 6401000N
Hema Atlas Map Ref 10 G11

276

Map 13 E5

Katikati Naturist Park

149 Wharawhara Rd, Katikati: not signposted from SH2
Ph 0800 456 567

2765600E 6400300N

Hema Atlas Map Ref 10 G11

277

Map 13 E5

Sapphire Springs Thermal Pools & Holiday Park

Hot Springs Rd, Katikati: signposted from SH2 at Katikati
Ph (07) 549 0768 sapphire.springs@xtra.co.nz

Author's note — A peaceful, rural and bush-clad alternative to the coastal crowds.

2764800E 6398300N

Hema Atlas Map Ref 10 H11

278

Map 13 E5

Omokoroa Tourist Park & Thermal Hot Pools

165 Omokoroa Beach Rd, Omokoroa Beach:
a 4km deviation NE of SH2
Ph (07) 548 0857 omokoroatp@xtra.co.nz

Author's note — Neat and tidy site that is handy to the estuary.

2777800E 6391900N

Hema Atlas Map Ref 10 H12

279

Map 13 E5

Te Puna Lodge Motel and Holiday Park

Cnr SH2 and Waihi Rd, Te Puna
Ph 0800 837 862 tepunamotel@xtra.co.nz

2780600E 6385800N

Hema Atlas Map Ref 10 J13

280

Map 13 E5

Roadside Rest Area

Adjacent SH2 on the S bank of the Wairoa River: visible
from the bridge

Swimming, picnicking, canoeing

2783400E 6385600N

Hema Atlas Map Ref 94 C1, 10 J13

281

Map 13 E5

Tauranga Tourist Park

9 Mayfair St, Tauranga: signposted W from SH2
N of the Waimapu Estuary
Ph/Fax (07) 578 3323 mayfair@wave.co.nz

Author's note — Clean and tidy site that's very handy
to Tauranga's city centre.

2789800E 6383500N

Hema Atlas Map Ref 94 C2, 10 J13

282

Map 13 E5

Silver Birch Family Holiday Park

101 Turret Rd, Tauranga: adjacent SH2 on the
N shore of Waimapu Estuary
Ph/Fax (07) 578 4603 silverbirch@xtra.co.nz

Author's note — Neat site on the water's edge.

2789800E 6383500N

Hema Atlas Map Ref 94 C2, 10 J13

283

Map 13 E5

Fernland Spa Thermal Mineral Springs

250 Cambridge Rd, Tauranga
Ph (07) 578 3081 www.fernlandspa.co.nz

2786200E 6383000N

Hema Atlas Map Ref 94 C1, 10 J13

284

Map 13 E5

Sanctuary Point Hot Pools and Camping Ground

Adjacent SH29, Tauranga: SW of the intersection with SH2
Ph (07) 544 0700 info@sanctuarypoint.co.nz

Author's note — More modern facilities than the other Tauranga options, and more spacious, but you pay extra for the pools.

2788300E 6381600N
Hema Atlas Map Ref 94 D2, 10 J13

SH25 Coromandel Peninsula — SH2 to Waihi

285

Map 12 E4

Roadside Rest Area

Kauaeranga Valley, SE of Thames

2741400E 6446300N
Hema Atlas Map Ref 8 H12

286

Map 12 E4

Kauaeranga Valley

14km E of Thames, Coromandel Forest Park
DoC Kauaeranga Visitor Centre Ph (07) 867 9080
kauaerangavc@doc.govt.nz

Eight areas: dogs only permitted at Hotoritori and Booms Flat

2740900E 6449000N
Hema Atlas Map Ref 8 H12

287

Map 12 E4

Kauaeranga Christian Camp

Kauaeranga SE of Thames: take the turnoff
to Parawai S of Thames
Ph (07) 868 8348

Author's note — Quiet rural location that's streamside for swimming.

2739900E 6447100N
Hema Atlas Map Ref 8 H11

288

Map 12 E4

Roadside Rest Area

SH25: just N of Thames

Author's note — Many similar picnic and rest areas along this coast north to Wilson Bay.

2733800E 6450800N
Hema Atlas Map Ref 8 G11

289

Map 12 D4

Dickson Holiday Park

Victoria Rd, Tararu: turnoff S of Tararu
Ph (07) 868 7308 reserve@dicksonpark.co.nz

Author's note — Sheltered valley location set in a reserve established in 1869. This camp includes a butterfly house and orchid garden.

2735600E 6451300N
Hema Atlas Map Ref 8 G11

290

Map 12 D4

Waiomu Domain Rest Area

Seaside along SH25 at Waiomu

2733800E 6459900N
Hema Atlas Map Ref 8 G11

291

Map 12 D4

Waiomu Bay Holiday Park

Waiomu Valley Rd, Waiomu: turnoff from SH25
at Waiomu Bay
Ph/Fax (07) 868 4710 ghumphrey@slingshot.co.nz

Author's note — Clean and tidy.

2735000E 6461500N
Hema Atlas Map Ref 8 F11

292 Tapu Creek Campervan Park

285 Tapu-Coroglen Rd: turnoff from SH25 at Tapu
Ph (07) 868 4560 tapucreek@clear.net.nz

Map 12 D4 Swimming stream nearby.

2734100E 6464900N
Hema Atlas Map Ref 8 F11

293 Tapu Motor Camp

SH25 at Tapu
Ph (07) 868 4837 ghumphrey@slingshot.co.nz

Author's note — Very popular beachfront location. It can get a tad
crowded, but to many that is the charm.

Map 12 D4

2734100E 6464900N
Hema Atlas Map Ref 8 F11

294 Roadside Rest Area

SH25 at Tapu

Map 12 D4 Author's note — Waterside picnic area.

2732300E 6466000N
Hema Atlas Map Ref 8 F11

295 Roadside Rest Area

SH25 at Waikawau: S of the stream

Map 12 D4 Author's note — Waterside picnic area.

2729900E 6469900N
Hema Atlas Map Ref 8 E11

296 Roadside Rest Area

SH25 at Wilson's Bay

Map 12 D4 Author's note — Waterside picnic area.

2726000E 6476300N
Hema Atlas Map Ref 8 E10

297 Tidewater Tourist Park

270 Tiki Rd, Coromandel: just S of Coromandel township
Ph (07) 866 8888 tidewater@world-net.co.nz

Author's note — Although this is more a motel than a campground
there's a small grassed area available if needed.

Map 12 D4

2733300E 6489200N
Hema Atlas Map Ref 8 D11

298 Tui Lodge

60 Whangapoua Rd, Coromandel: about 800m
E of Coromandel township
Ph (07) 866 8237 tuilodge@paradise.net.nz

Author's note — More suited to camping than motorhomes, but
it's a lovely spot favoured by backpackers, cyclists and motorcyclists.

Map 12 D4

2734500E 6491100N
Hema Atlas Map Ref 8 C11

299 Coromandel Motels & Holiday Park

636 Rings Rd, Coromandel: main road, N of Coromandel
Ph (07) 866 8830
addressenquiries@coromandelholidaypark.co.nz

Author's note — Neat and tidy site, and the closest camp to
Coromandel township.

Map 12 D4

2733200E 6491600N
Hema Atlas Map Ref 8 C11

300

Map 12 D4

Long Bay Motor Camp

3200 Long Bay Rd, Long Bay: signposted from
the centre of Coromandel
Ph (07) 866 8720 lbmccoromandel@xtra.co.nz

Author's note — A magic location, ideal for anglers and swimmers,
although the camp itself would rate about three star.

2732000E 6492200N

Hema Atlas Map Ref 8 C11

301

Map 12 D4

Shelly Beach Top 10 Holiday Park

243 Colville Rd: N of Coromandel township
Ph 0800 424 655 shelly@world-net.co.nz

Author's note — Well-managed camp in a nice waterfront location.

2732600E 6493900N

Hema Atlas Map Ref 8 C11

302

Map 12 D4

Oamaru Bay Motor Camp

440 Colville Rd: N of Coromandel township
Ph/Fax (07) 866 8735 oamaru.holiday.bay@xtra.co.nz

Author's note — A beautiful spot, just across the road from the beach.

2731400E 6494600N

Hema Atlas Map Ref 8 C11

303

Map 12 D4

Papaaroha Motor Camp

Beachside on Colville Rd, Papaaroha
Ph/Fax (07) 866 8818 fish@papaaroha.co.nz

Author's note — Another beautiful beachside spot, but it can
get a bit crowded.

         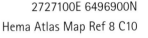

2727100E 6496900N

Hema Atlas Map Ref 8 C10

304

Map 12 D4

Anglers Lodge Motels & Holiday Park

Colville Rd, Amodeo Bay
Ph (07) 866 8584

Author's note — Very good facilities, just opposite a rocky beach
and handy to good fishing. Qualmark equivalent of at least four stars,
and such quality is relatively rare on this coast.

2728000E 6500400N

Hema Atlas Map Ref 8 B11

305

Map 12 D4

Colville Farm

Just S of Colville township
Ph/Fax (07) 866 6820

Author's note — Simple camping in a rural location, and horse
treks are available.

2733000E 6503600N

Hema Atlas Map Ref 8 B11

306

Map 12 D4

Colville Bay Motel & Motor Camp

Wharf Rd: NW of Colville
Ph/Fax (07) 866 6814 colvillemotel@xtra.co.nz

2730900E 6504300N

Hema Atlas Map Ref 8 B11

307

Map 12 D4

Roadside Rest Area

Author's note — Waterside picnic area.

2730900E 6505900N

Hema Atlas Map Ref 8 B11

308 Otautu Bay Motor Camps

Bayside at Otautu

Map 12 D4

A caretaker may collect koha or fees if they are in attendance. Author's note — Beautiful beachside location, with several spots to choose from.

2729700E 6507600N
Hema Atlas Map Ref 8 B10

---

309 Fantail Bay

Off Port Jackson Rd en route to Port Jackson:
44km N of Coromandel
DoC Kauaeranga Visitor Centre Ph (07) 867 9080
kauaerangavc@doc.govt.nz

Map 12 D4

Self registration system; cold showers only; fishing, diving, swimming.
Author's note — Sheltered pohutakawa-clad valley leading to a sheltered stony beach.

2719800E 6517600N
Hema Atlas Map Ref 8 A9

---

310 Port Jackson

Beachside at Port Jackson: 50km N of Coromandel
DoC Kauaeranga Visitor Centre Ph (07) 867 9080
kauaerangavc@doc.govt.nz

Map 12 D4

Self registration system; cold showers only.
Author's note — More open camping than Fantail Bay, but located right on the beachfront. A tranquil spot.

2720000E 6522100N
Hema Atlas Map Ref 8 A9

---

311 Fletcher Bay

Off Fletcher Bay Rd: 53km N of Coromandel
DoC Kauaeranga Visitor Centre Ph (07) 867 9080
kauaerangavc@doc.govt.nz

Map 12 D4

Cold showers only

2724700E 6521500N
Hema Atlas Map Ref 8 A10

---

312 Stony Bay

Stony Bay Rd, off Port Charles Rd: 45km N of Coromandel
DoC Kauaeranga Visitor Centre Ph (07) 867 9080
kauaerangavc@doc.govt.nz

Map 12 D4

Cold showers only

2726700E 6517600N
Hema Atlas Map Ref 8 A10

---

313 Waikawau Bay

Off Waikawau Beach Rd: 36km N of Coromandel
DoC Kauaeranga Visitor Centre Ph (07) 867 9080
kauaerangavc@doc.govt.nz

Map 12 D4

Bookings required for December & January: Ph (07) 866 1106

2736100E 6509200N
Hema Atlas Map Ref 8 B11

---

314 Kuaotunu Motor Camp

33 Bluff Rd, Kuaotunu West: signposted from SH25,
W end of Kuaotunu Bay
Ph (07) 866 5628 mikesavage@xtra.co.nz

Map 13 D5

Author's note — A nice spot opposite the very pretty beach, and backing onto a small stream.

2751400E 6494000N
Hema Atlas Map Ref 8 C13

315 Roadside Rest Area

Alongside Kuaotunu Bay

2752600E 6494400N
Hema Atlas Map Ref 8 C13

Map 13 D5   Author's note — Waterside picnic area.

---

316 Roadside Rest Area

Alongside Kuaotunu Bay

2753800E 6494700N
Hema Atlas Map Ref 8 C13

Map 13 D5   Author's note — Waterside picnic area.

---

317 Otama Beach Reserve Picnic Area

Signposted from Kuaotunu: 10km via gravel road

2755400E 6496100N
Hema Atlas Map Ref 8 C13

Map 13 D5   Author's note — Overnight camping not allowed.

---

318 Otama Beach Camping Ground

Signposted from Kuaotunui: 10km via gravel road
Ph (07) 866 2872

2756600E 6496000N
Hema Atlas Map Ref 8 C13

Map 13 D5   Author's note — Opposite a beautiful beach this farmer's property offers simple and sheltered camping.

---

319 Roadside Rest Area

Alongside SH25: S of Kuaotunu

2754700E 6491000N
Hema Atlas Map Ref 8 C13

Map 13 D5

---

320 Simpsons Beach (Wharekaho Beach)

Alongside SH25: N end of the bay
NZ Motor Caravan Association Ph (09) 298 5466
www.nzmca.org.nz

2754200E 6487000N
Hema Atlas Map Ref 8 D13

Map 13 D5   Private camping via the NZ Motor Caravan Association

---

321 Roadside Rest Area

Alongside SH25: N of Whitianga

2754100E 6485400N
Hema Atlas Map Ref 8 D13

Map 13 D5

---

322 Aladdin Holiday Park

55 Bongard Rd, Whitianga: signposted from SH25
N end of Mercury Bay, about 1.2km from Whitianga
Ph (07) 866 5834

2750500E 6484300N
Hema Atlas Map Ref 8 D13

Map 13 D5   Author's note — Cute cottages in a sheltered valley a mere stone's throw from the beach.

323
Map 13 D5

Mercury Bay Motor Camp & Holiday Park
121 Albert St, Whitianga: signposted from S end
of Whitianga town centre
Ph/Fax (07) 866 5579
Author's note — Handy to boat launching and the town centre

2751300E 6481000N
Hema Atlas Map Ref 8 D13

324
Map 13 D5

Harbourside Holiday Park
135 Albert St, Whitianga: signposted from S end
of Whitianga town centre
Ph/Fax (07) 866 5746 tomanddi@ihug.co.nz
Author's note — Handy to boat launching and the town centre.

2751300E 6481000N
Hema Atlas Map Ref 8 D13

325
Map 13 D5

Riverglen Motor Park & Lodge
Tapu Coroglen Rd, Coroglen: off SH25
Ph (07) 866 3130 Fax (07) 866 3290
www.whitianga.co.nz/riverglen riverglen@xtra.co.nz

2750600E 6472600N
Hema Atlas Map Ref 8 E13

326
Map 13 D5

Shakespeare's Scenic Reserve
Off Purangi Rd, from SH25: signposted NW of Cooks Beach

2754200E 6482300N
Hema Atlas Map Ref 8 D13

327
Map 13 D5

Hahei Holiday Resort
Approximately 14km N of SH25 from Whenuakite:
signposted from Hahei town centre
Ph (07) 866 3889 info@haheiholidays.co.nz
Fishing, swimming, boating Author's note — Beautiful beachside
location. Make sure you do the one hour walk to Cathedral Cove.

2761100E 6480500N
Hema Atlas Map Ref 8 D14

328
Map 13 D5

Roadside Rest Area
Alongside SH25, Coromandel Forest Park

2761500E 6468700N
Hema Atlas Map Ref 8 F14

329
Map 13 D5

Kauri Grove Lookout & Scenic Reserve
Alongside SH25 N of Tairua

2762200E 6467400N
Hema Atlas Map Ref 8 F14

330
Map 13 D5

Roadside Rest Area
Waterfront Tairua

Author's note — Waterside picnic area.

2765200E 6464400N
Hema Atlas Map Ref 8 F14

331

Map 13 D5

Tairua Holiday Park

Manaia Rd: in the centre of Tairua
Ph/Fax (07) 864 8071

Author's note — Compact camp conveniently located between
the town centre and beach.

2764600E 6462900N
Hema Atlas Map Ref 8 F14

332

Map 13 D5

The Glade Holiday Park

68 Vista Paku, Pauanui: signposted from Pauanui
town centre
Ph (07) 864 8559 info@pauanui-glade.co.nz

2764300E 6460000N
Hema Atlas Map Ref 8 G14

333

Map 13 D5

Roadside Rest Area

Pauanui

2765100E 6458700N
Hema Atlas Map Ref 8 G14

334

Map 13 D5

Broken Hills

4km off SH25, on Hikaui/Puketui Rd
DoC Kauaeranga Visitor Centre Ph (07) 867 9080
kauaerangavc@doc.govt.nz

Swimming, fishing, walking; self registration system

2753000E 6451000N
Hema Atlas Map Ref 8 G13

335

Map 13 D5

Opoutere Motor Camp

5km NE of SH25 at Opoutere: follow Opoutere Rd off SH25,
signposted at the end of the tarseal
Ph/Fax (07) 865 9152 info@opouterebeach.co.nz

Author's note — Simple camping with easy access to a good
surfing beach, backing onto a peaceful estuary and surrounded
by DoC wildlife reserves.

2765500E 6451800N
Hema Atlas Map Ref 8 G14

336

Map 13 E5

Whangamata Motor Camp

104 Barbara Ave, Whangamata: signposted from
the town centre
Ph (07) 865 9128

Author's note — The handiest to the town centre and the
beach, but it is busy.

2765000E 6439900N
Hema Atlas Map Ref 8 J14

337

Map 13 E5

Settlers Motor Camp

101 Leander Rd, Whangamata: signposted from Port Rd,
just S of the township
Ph/Fax (07) 865 8181 settlersmotorcamp@clear.net.nz

2765000E 6439900N
Hema Atlas Map Ref 8 J14

338

Map 13 E5

Pinefield Holiday Park

207 Port Rd, Whangamata: at the S end of Whangamata,
not far from the junction with SH25
Ph/Fax (07) 865 8791 whangamatatop10@xtra.co.nz

Author's note — My pick of the central Whangamata locations because
it has park-like grounds with heaps of space and isn't too far from the
beaches and town centre.

2765000E 6439900N
Hema Atlas Map Ref 8 J14

339

Map 13 E5

Wentworth Valley

Off SH25 S of Whangamata
DoC Kauaeranga Visitor Centre Ph (07) 867 9080
kauaerangavc@doc.govt.nz

Self registration system. Author's note — A rural alternative to the crowds of Whangamata, yet still handy to the beach.

2761100E 6435100N
Hema Atlas Map Ref 8 J14

SH1 — Hamilton to Taupo

340

Map 12 E4

Roadside Rest Area

Hamilton Gardens: riverside from SH1 E of the town centre

2713500E 6374600N
Hema Atlas Map Ref 92 G4, 11 C7

341

Map 15 A5

Cambridge Motor Park

332 Scott St, Leamington: signposted from SH1
E of Cambridge across the river at Leamington
Ph/Fax (07) 827 6649
cambridgemotorpark@paradise.net.nz

Author's note — Huge park-like grounds adjoining a public domain.

2728200E 6363300N
Hema Atlas Map Ref 12 D8

342

Map 15 A5

Roadside Rest Area

Adjacent SH1 and Lake Karapiro

Author's note — Lakeside picnic area.

2734300E 6361200N
Hema Atlas Map Ref 12 D9

343

Map 15 A5

Lake Karapiro Camping & Pursuits Centre

601 Maungatautari Road, Cambridge: adjacent
Lake Karapiro
Ph (07) 827 4178 karapiro@xtra.co.nz

Author's note — Handy to the Lake Karapiro rowing venue.

2733100E 6360800N
Hema Atlas Map Ref 12 D9

344

Map 15 A5

Roadside Rest Area

Adjacent SH1 and Lake Karapiro

Author's note — Lakeside picnic area.

2738000E 6357900N
Hema Atlas Map Ref 12 E9

345

Map 15 A5

Roadside Rest Area

Adjacent SH1 and Lake Karapiro

Author's note — Lakeside picnic area.

2739200E 6357700N
Hema Atlas Map Ref 12 E9

346

Map 15 A5

Roadside Rest Area

Alongside Maungatauri Rd and Lake Karapiro

Author's note — Lakeside picnic area.

2743100E 6356800N
Hema Atlas Map Ref 12 E10

347

Map 15 A5

Roadside Rest Area
Adjacent SH27

2751600E 6358300N
Hema Atlas Map Ref 12 E11

348

Map 13 E5

Opal Hot Springs Holiday Park
Okauia Springs Rd, Okauia: 5km NE of Matamata, follow
the signs to the Tower Museum and carry on another 2km
Ph (07) 888 8198 www.opalhotsprings.com

2759600E 6376700N
Hema Atlas Map Ref 12 C11

349

Map 15 A5

Kea Motel & Holiday Park
SH1: N end of Putaruru
Ph/Fax (07) 882 1590

Author's note — Basically an add-on to the motel but useful.

2753700E 6347800N
Hema Atlas Map Ref 12 F11

350

Map 15 B5

Tokoroa Motor Camp
22 Sloss Rd, Tokoroa: N end of Tokoroa,
signposted from SH1
Ph (07) 886 6642 tokoroa.camp@orcon.net.nz
Author's note — A small camp, perhaps best suited to permanents.

2762400E 6328500N
Hema Atlas Map Ref 12 H12

351

Map 15 B5

Roadside Rest & Camping Area
Along SH30, Dunham Point, Lake Whakamaru: signposted
W of SH30 & SH1 intersection
Author's note — Overnight camping is allowed but there are few facili-
ties other than shelter and shade in a picturesque lakeside location.

2762800E 6305700N
Hema Atlas Map Ref 19 A4

352

Map 15 B5

Roadside Rest Area
Along SH30, beside the dam at Whakamaru

2755800E 6304800N
Hema Atlas Map Ref 19 A3

353

Map 15 B5

Roadside Rest Area
Along SH32 at Whakamaru

Author's note — Lakeside picnic area.

2754700E 6306400N
Hema Atlas Map Ref 19 A3

354

Map 15 B5

Waipapa Road Rest Area

Waipapa Rd: beside Lake Arapuni
Author's note — Several potential overnight casual camping options in
this pretty area.

2744500E 6319300N
Hema Atlas Map Ref 12 J10

355

Map 15 B5

Ngaherenga

Off SH30, adjacent to Pureora Forest Park Headquarters
DoC Kauaeranga Visitor Centre Ph (07) 867 9080
kauaerangavc@doc.govt.nz

2732100E 6294400N
Hema Atlas Map Ref 18 B13

356
Map 15 B5

Kakaho

Link Rd from Pureora Forest Park Headquarters;
or Kakaho Rd from SH32
DoC Kauaeranga Visitor Centre Ph (07) 867 9080
kauaerangavc@doc.govt.nz

2746200E 6288900N
Hema Atlas Map Ref 19 C2

357
Map 15 C5

Roadside Rest Area

E of SH32

Author's note — Scenic views.

2744300E 6263700N
Hema Atlas Map Ref 19 E2

358
Map 15 B5

Wairakei Thermal Valley

Signposted from SH5 at Wairakei: 8km NE from Taupo
Ph (07) 374 8004

2779900E 6284800N
Hema Atlas Map Ref 19 C5

359
Map 15 B5

Huka Falls Scenic Reserve

Follow signs from SH5 N of Taupo to Huka Falls
Author's note — A short walk to view these pretty falls.

2779800E 6279600N
Hema Atlas Map Ref 19 D5

360
Map 15 B5

Reids Farm Recreation Reserve

Follow signs from SH5 N of Taupo to Huka Falls:
camp adjoins the Huka Falls Rd and the River
Ph (07) 376 0617

Free summer camping allowed, but only from October 1 to April 31
(maximum length of stay is 28 days) Author's note — Simple camping in
a magnificent setting, and the swimming pools are magnificent.

2779200E 6278100N
Hema Atlas Map Ref 19 D5

SH2 — Tauranga to Opotiki

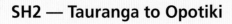

361
Map 13 E5

Mt Maunganui Domain Motor Camp

Adams Ave, Mt Maunganui: beachfront right
under the Mt Mauao
Ph (07) 575 4471 mtdomain@xtra.co.nz

Author's note — The fabulous location outweighs rather tired facilities
and it's best to avoid the Christmas and New Year crowds. Otherwise
a great base for boating, fishing, surfing or walking Mauao.

2790100E 6392300N
Hema Atlas Map Ref 94 A3, 13 A4

362
Map 13 E5

Cosy Corner Holiday Park

40 Ocean Beach Rd, Mt Maunganui
Ph (07) 575 5899 cosycorner@clear.net.nz

Author's note — Just opposite the beach, and handy to Mt Maunganui
although big rigs may struggle with the entrance.

2793900E 6389500N
Hema Atlas Map Ref 94 B3, 13 B4

363

Map 13 E5

Golden Grove Holiday Park

73 Girven Rd, Mt Maunganui
Ph (07) 575 5821
Author's note — A very neat and tidy 'newish' camp that's handy to the beach.

2795200E 6387400N
Hema Atlas Map Ref 94 B4, 13 B4

364

Map 13 E5

Beach Grove Holiday Park

386 Papamoa Beach Rd, Papamoa
Ph (07) 572 1337 bg2000@xtra.co.nz
Author's note — New facilities in a neat and tidy park, although it's quite suburban.

2798800E 6385700N
Hema Atlas Map Ref 94 C5, 13 B4

365

Map 13 E5

Papamoa Beach Top 10 Holiday Resort

535 Papamoa Beach Rd, Papamoa
Ph (07) 572 0816 resort@papamoa.beach.co.nz
Author's note — A beautiful camp in a magic location, and the five star Qualmark rating makes it a nice treat.

2800300E 6384900N
Hema Atlas Map Ref 94 C5, 13 B5

366

Map 13 E5

Papamoa Village Park

267 Parton Rd, Papamoa
Ph (07) 542 1890
Author's note — Neat and tidy in park-like grounds, but this popular site can get crowded at peak times.

2801600E 6381100N
Hema Atlas Map Ref 94 D5, 13 B5

367

Map 13 E5

Te Puke Holiday Park

SH2: W of Te Puke
Ph/Fax (07) 573 9866
Author's note — Sheltered, but close to a very busy road.

2800700E 6375700N
Hema Atlas Map Ref 13 C5

368

Map 13 E5

Beech Caravan Park

Off SH2 at Little Waihi: at the shopping centre
Ph (07) 533 2165
Author's note — The location is magic but this camp is being overtaken by motel units and cabins, so it is better suited to campervans than camping.

2814600E 6378000N
Hema Atlas Map Ref 13 C6

369

Map 13 E5

Bledisloe Holiday Park

Off SH2 at Little Waihi
Ph (07) 533 2157
Author's note — This is a fabulous location but the camp is tired, which is a great shame as this spot is hard to beat.

2816300E 6377400N
Hema Atlas Map Ref 13 C6

370

Map 13 E5

Bay Views Holiday Park & Motels

195 Arawa Ave, Maketu
Ph/Fax (07) 533 2222 troutpool@xtra.co.nz
Author's note — Although this is the most distant camp from the area's beaches this is compensated for by it being so good.

2816100E 6375700N
Hema Atlas Map Ref 13 C6

371

Map 15 A6

Paengaroa Motor Lodge

1km S of the SH33/SH2 intersection
Ph (07) 533 1170 paengaroa.motels@xtra.co.nz

2811000E 6371000N
Hema Atlas Map Ref 13 C6

372

Map 13 E6

Pukehina Motor Camp

27 Costello Cres, Pukehina
Ph (07) 533 3600

Author's note — Compact and tidy with a few permanents.

2820500E 6372900N
Hema Atlas Map Ref 13 C7

373

Map 15 A6

Beachfront reserve

Beachside on SH2 near Waitahanui Stream

2827700E 6368700N
Hema Atlas Map Ref 13 D7

374

Map 15 A6

Pikowai Reserve Camping Ground

Shoreside SH2 at Pikowai
Whakatane District Council Ph (07) 306 0500

Self registration system Author's note — Beachside with plenty of shelter and shade.

2833300E 6365800N
Hema Atlas Map Ref 14 D8

375

Map 15 A6

Murphy's Holiday Camp

Shoreside on SH2 W of Matata
Ph (07) 322 2136

Author's note — This cosy beachside camp is actually quite big and popular.

2838500E 6363300N
Hema Atlas Map Ref 14 D8

376

Map 15 A6

Matata Domain Camp

Alongside SH2 at Matata
Ph (07) 322 2327

Author's note — Simple camping in a great spot and it's cheap too.

2840600E 6362300N
Hema Atlas Map Ref 14 D9

377

Map 15 B6

Waimana Valley 8 Acre

Waimana Valley, Te Urewera National Park
DoC Aniwaniwa Visitor Centre Ph (06) 837 3803
urewerainfo@doc.govt.nz

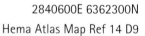

2870300E 6324700N
Hema Atlas Map Ref 14 H12

378

Map 15 A7

Ohiwa Family Holiday Park

Ohiwa: signposted as a 9km diversion W from SH2
Ph/Fax (07) 315 4741 ohiwa-holidays@xtra.co.nz

Author's note — All the benefits of Ohope, but without the crowds. By reclaiming coastal erosion, this holiday park has won several environmental awards.

2876400E 6348200N
Hema Atlas Map Ref 14 F12

379

Map 15 A7

Roadside Rest Area

Author's note — Several roadside and seaside rest areas east of this vicinity along the beautiful pohutakawa-clad coastline.

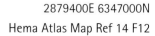

2879400E 6347000N
Hema Atlas Map Ref 14 F12

380

Map 15 A7

Island View Family Holiday Park
Appleton Rd, Waiotahi Beach: W of Opotiki
Ph/Fax (07) 315 7519 islandview@xtra.co.nz

Author's note — Close to a pretty beach and good fishing.

2883400E 6348500N
Hema Atlas Map Ref 14 F13

381

Map 15 A7

Opotiki Holiday Park
Potts Ave, Opotiki: signposted from the city centre
Ph/Fax (07) 315 6050 opotiki-holiday@xtra.co.nz

Author's note — The closest camp to the city centre yet pretty quiet, clean and tidy.

2885900E 6347100N
Hema Atlas Map Ref 14 F13

SH30 — Whakatane to Rotorua

382

Map 15 A6

Whakatane Caravan Park & Motor Camp
Signposted from SH30 at W end of Whakatane
Ph (07) 308 8694 whak@xtra.co.nz

Author's note — Close to the beach set in park-like grounds this is a big camp and the handiest to the centre of Whakatane.

2860800E 6354000N
Hema Atlas Map Ref 14 E11

383

Map 15 A6

Thornton Beach Motor Camp
163 Thornton Beach Rd, Thornton: W of Whakatane
Ph/Fax (07) 304 8296

Author's note — Beachside and handy to the river mouth for boating and fishing.

2850300E 6359000N
Hema Atlas Map Ref 14 E10

384

Map 15 A6

Roadside Rest Area
Thornton Beach Reserve, Thornton: NW of Whakatane

2851500E 6359000N
Hema Atlas Map Ref 14 E10

385

Map 15 A6

Ohope Beach Top 10
(Surf & Sand Holiday Park)
Harbour Rd: E of Ohope township, E of Whakatane
Ph 0800 264 673 ohopebeach@xtra.co.nz

Author's note — Beachside for swimming, surfing and fishing, and boat launching nearby.

2871500E 6350200N
Hema Atlas Map Ref 14 F12

386

Map 15 A6

Ohope Beach Picnic Areas
W end of Ohope Beach: E of Whakatane

Author's note — There are several reserves in this vicinity with toilets and cold water showers for beach goers. No camping allowed.

2872700E 6350200N
Hema Atlas Map Ref 14 F12

387

Map 15 A6

Awakeri Hot Springs
Beside SH30: 23km SW of Whakatane
Ph (07) 304 9117 awakeri.springs@wave.co.nz

Author's note — A peaceful, bush-clad setting with hot springs.

2849500E 6346800N
Hema Atlas Map Ref 14 F9

388 Map 15 B6

Matahi Spit Reserve

At the E end of Lake Rotoma: signposted off SH30

2826200E 6343100N
Hema Atlas Map Ref 13 F7

389 Map 15 B6

Roadside Rest Area

Beside Lake Rotoma & SH30

2825000E 6342800N
Hema Atlas Map Ref 13 F7

390 Map 15 A6

Roadside Rest Area

Beside Lake Rotoma & SH30

2823800E 6344600N
Hema Atlas Map Ref 13 F7

391 Map 15 A6

Rotoma Holiday Park

Signposted from SH30 at Lake Rotoma
Ph/Fax (07) 362 0815 peter-john@slingshot.co.nz

Author's note — Soda water mineral pools nearby.

2821800E 6345800N
Hema Atlas Map Ref 13 F7

392 Map 15 A6

Roadside Rest Area

Beside Lake Rotoiti and SH30

2818300E 6346600N
Hema Atlas Map Ref 13 F6

393 Map 15 A6

Roadside Rest Area

Beside Lake Rotoiti and SH30

2816200E 6346500N
Hema Atlas Map Ref 13 F6

394 Map 15 A6

Roadside Rest Area

Beside Lake Rotoiti and SH30

2815400E 6345300N
Hema Atlas Map Ref 13 F6

395 Map 15 B6

Roadside Rest Area

Beside Lake Rotoiti and SH30

2811200E 6344600N
Hema Atlas Map Ref 13 F6

396 Map 15 B6

All Seasons Holiday Park

50-58 Loe Rd, Hannah's Bay: signposted off SH30
near the airport
Ph 0800 422 674 allseasonsrotorua@xtra.co.nz

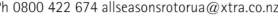

2800600E 6337700N
Hema Atlas Map Ref 96 B5, 13 G5

397 Holdens Bay Top 10 Holiday Park

Map 15 B6

7 Stonebridge Park, Holdens Bay: signposted
off SH30 near the airport
Ph 0800 14 88 84 accommodation@holdensbay.co.nz
Author's note — Sparkling new amenities.

2799400E 6337300N

Hema Atlas Map Ref 96 B5, 13 G4

398 Redwood Holiday Park

Map 15 B6

5 Tarawera Rd: signposted at Blue Lake, turnoff SH30
Ph/Fax (07) 345 9380 reservations@redwoodpark.co.nz
Author's note — Although it's near a major road there's good
walking to be had nearby.

2797300E 6333200N

Hema Atlas Map Ref 96 C4, 13 G4

399 Blue Lake Top 10 Holiday Park

Map 15 B6

923 Tarawera Rd: follow signs to Blue Lake
Ph 0800 808 292 bluelaketop10@xtra.co.nz
Author's note — Swimming, fishing, boating and walking opportunities
abound in this very tranquil setting. It's hard to believe you are so
close to Rotorua.

2802300E 6330400N

Hema Atlas Map Ref 13 H5

400 Lake Tarawera Outlet

Map 15 B6

Eastern shore of Lake Tarawera (boat access); vehicle access
via Kawerau requires a permit from Fletcher Challenge
Forest Information Centre in Rotorua
DoC www.doc.govt.nz or Tourism Rotorua Ph (07) 348 5170
tourism.rotorua@rdc.govt.nz

2817200E 6328500N

Hema Atlas Map Ref 13 H6

401 Hot Water Beach

Map 15 B6

Te Rata Bay, Lake Tarawera (boat access only)
DoC www.doc.govt.nz or Tourism Rotorua Ph (07) 348 5170
tourism.rotorua@rdc.govt.nz

2812800E 6323100N

Hema Atlas Map Ref 13 H6

402 Rotorua Thermal Holiday Park

Map 15 B5

Old Taupo Rd, Rotorua: S end near junction with SH5
Ph (07) 346 3140 holidayparkrotorua@xtra.co.nz
Author's note — A lovely location: one of the most impressive
camps in Rotorua.

2793900E 6333100N

Hema Atlas Map Ref 96 D3, 13 G4

403 Rotorua Top 10 Holiday Park

Map 15 B5

1495 Pukuatua St, Rotorua: several blocks from
the city centre
Ph 0800 22 32 67 stay@rotoruatop10.co.nz
Author's note — The handiest to the centre of Rotorua.

2793700E 6335700N

Hema Atlas Map Ref 96 C3, 13 G4

404 Cosy Cottage International Holiday Park

Map 15 B5

67 Whittaker Rd, Rotorua: lakeside N of Rotorua city
centre, signposted from SH5
Ph 0800 22 24 24 cosycottage@xtra.co.nz

2794400E 6337400N

Hema Atlas Map Ref 96 B3, 13 G4

405

Map 15 B5

Rotorua Lakeside Thermal Holiday Park

54 Whittaker Rd, Rotorua: lakeside N of Rotorua city
centre, signposted from SH5
Ph/Fax (07) 348 1693 relax@rotorualakesidethermal.co.nz

2794400E 6337400N

Hema Atlas Map Ref 96 B3, 13 G4

406

Map 15 B5

Willowhaven Holiday Park

31 Beaumont Rd: lakeside N of Rotorua, signposted
from SH5 at Ngongotaha
Ph (07) 357 4092 info@willowhaven.co.nz

2792800E 6341300N

Hema Atlas Map Ref 13 F4

407

Map 15 B5

Rotorua Family Holiday Park aka Rainbow Resort Holiday Park

22 Beaumont Rd: lakeside N of Rotorua, signposted
from SH5 at Ngongotaha
Ph 0800 574 259 stay@rotoruafamilypark.co.nz

2792800E 6341300N

Hema Atlas Map Ref 13 F4

408

Map 15 B5

Waiteti Trout Stream Holiday Park

14 Okona Cres, Waiteti: signposted N of Rotorua
on lake loop road
Ph (07) 357 5255 waiteti.trout.hp@xtra.co.nz
Author's note — Sheltered, quiet location handy to a fishing stream.

2792300E 6343400N

Hema Atlas Map Ref 13 F4

409

Map 15 A5

Roadside Rest Area

Hamurana Springs Recreation Reserve, Hamurana:
N side of Lake Rotorua

2795700E 6347700N

Hema Atlas Map Ref 13 F4

410

Map 15 A6

Roadside Rest Area

Of SH33: N of Lake Rotoiti near Okere Falls

2803600E 6346100N

Hema Atlas Map Ref 13 F5

411

Map 15 A6

Lake Rotoiti Lakeside Holiday Park

Okere Rd, Okere Falls: off SH33, N of Okere Falls
Ph (07) 362 4860 lakerotoiti@xtra.co.nz
Author's note — Good canoeing and rafting to be had on the
Okere Falls, and the nearby fishing is also very good.

2804400E 6349400N

Hema Atlas Map Ref 13 F5

SH5 & SH38 — Rotorua to Wairoa

412

Map 15 B5

Roadside Rest Area

SH5: S of Rotorua

2795700E 6330900N

Hema Atlas Map Ref 13 G4

413 Maungaongaonga Scenic Reserve

Just S of junction of SH5 & SH38

Map 15 B6

Author's note — A pretty stopping point.

2804600E 6315800N
Hema Atlas Map Ref 13 J5

414 The Living Waters of Waikite Valley Thermal Pools

Follow signs to the Waikite Valley from SH5:
29km from Rotorua
Ph/Fax (07) 333 1861 thermalpools@xtra.co.nz

Map 15 B5

Author's note — A pretty rural location for these thermal pools,
well away from the Rotorua crowds and well worth checking out.

2795100E 6311900N
Hema Atlas Map Ref 13 J4

415 Guy Roe Reserve (Homestead Arm)

Guy Roe Reserve, on Brett Rd alongside Lake
Rerewhakaaitu: follow signs from SH38 to Mt Tarawera
Rotorua District Council Parks & Recreation
Ph (07) 348 4199

Map 15 B6

Author's note — Lakeside for swimming, fishing and boating and
handy to Rotorua yet peaceful.

2815500E 6317500N
Hema Atlas Map Ref 13 J6

416 Rerewhakaaitu — Ashpit Road (Ash Pit Bay)

Rerewhakaaitu Rd off SH38, then follow Ash Pit Rd,
alongside Lake Rerewhakaaitu: 29km SE of Rotorua
DoC Rotorua Lakes Area Office Ph (07) 348 3610
www.doc.govt.nz or Tourism Rotorua Ph (07) 348 5170
tourism.rotorua@rdc.govt.nz
Self registration applies

Map 15 B6

2817000E 6318300N
Hema Atlas Map Ref 13 J6

417 Rerewhakaaitu — Bretts Road (Awaatua Bay)

Rerewhakaaitu Rd off SH38, then follow Brett Rd,
alongside Lake Rerewhakaaitu: 29km SE of Rotorua
DoC Rotorua Lakes Area Office Ph (07) 348 3610
www.doc.govt.nz or Tourism Rotorua Ph (07) 348 5170
tourism.rotorua@rdc.govt.nz
Self registration applies

Map 15 B6

2815400E 6319200N
Hema Atlas Map Ref 13 J6

418 Roadside Rest Area

Murapara: alongside the river

Map 15 B6

2833500E 6299000N
Hema Atlas Map Ref 20 B11

419 Roadside Rest Area With Camping

Alongside road to Lake Waikaremoana

Map 15 B6

Author's note — Nice riverside spot, signposted as
allowing 'free' camping.

2839500E 6286100N
Hema Atlas Map Ref 20 C11

north island camping sites

420 Mangamate

Map 15 B6

Minginui Rd off SH38: 90km SE of Rotorua
DoC www.doc.govt.nz or Tourism Rotorua Ph (07) 348 5170
tourism.rotorua@rdc.govt.nz
Drinking water is from a stream

2834300E 6279300N
Hema Atlas Map Ref 20 D11

421 Okahu

Map 15 B6

Okahu Rd, off SH38: 105km SE of Rotorua
DoC www.doc.govt.nz or Tourism Rotorua Ph (07) 348 5170
tourism.rotorua@rdc.govt.nz
Drinking water is from stream

2841300E 6275400N
Hema Atlas Map Ref 20 D12

422 Mimiha Bridge

Map 15 B6

Adjacent SH38: SW of Ruatahuna
DoC Aniwaniwa Visitor Centre Ph (06) 837 3803
urewerainfo@doc.govt.nz
Swimming, fishing. Author's note — One of the few genuine 'free-camping' spots.

2851800E 6275900N
Hema Atlas Map Ref 20 D13

423 Roadside Rest Area

Map 15 B6

Mano-o-rongo Stream

2856100E 6279400N
Hema Atlas Map Ref 20 D13

424 Roadside Rest Area

Map 15 B6

Roadside for Rest Area for Whakatakaa Hut Track

2861600E 6278900N
Hema Atlas Map Ref 20 D13

425 Orangihikoia, Te Urewera National Park

Map 15 B6

SH38, north of Lake Waikaremoana: roadside at Orangihikoia Stream
DoC Aniwaniwa Visitor Centre Ph (06) 837 3803
urewerainfo@doc.govt.nz
Drinking water is from a stream

2862300E 6274300N
Hema Atlas Map Ref 20 D14

426 Te Taita O Makora, Te Urewera National Park

Map 15 B6

Adjacent SH38, N of Waikaremoana
DoC Aniwaniwa Visitor Centre Ph (06) 837 3803
urewerainfo@doc.govt.nz

2863800E 6272100N
Hema Atlas Map Ref 20 D14

427 Mokau Landing, Te Urewera National Park

Map 15 C6

At Lake Waikaremoana, adjacent SH38: N of Waikaremoana
DoC Aniwaniwa Visitor Centre Ph (06) 837 3803
urewerainfo@doc.govt.nz
Swimming, boating, tramping, fishing

2864900E 6265800N
Hema Atlas Map Ref 20 E14

428
Map 15 C6

Waikaremoana Motor Camp, Te Urewera National Park

Home Bay at Lake Waikaremoana, adjacent SH38
DoC Aniwaniwa Visitor Centre Ph (06) 837 3803
urewerainfo@doc.govt.nz; Bookings Ph (06) 837 3826

Swimming, boating, tramping, fishing

2870200E 6264200N
Hema Atlas Map Ref 21 E2

429
Map 15 C6

Whaitiri Point Rest Area

Roadside at Lake Waikaremoana (SH38)

2869700E 6263000N
Hema Atlas Map Ref 21 E2

430
Map 15 C6

Onepoto Caves Walk Rest Area

Alongside road to Lake Waikaremoana (SH38)

2867500E 6259800N
Hema Atlas Map Ref 21 F2

431
Map 15 C6

Big Bush Holiday Park

Alongside road to Lake Waikaremoana (SH38): S of Onepoto
Ph (06) 837 7377

Author's note — Nice views of a small lake.

2869800E 6258100N
Hema Atlas Map Ref 21 F2

432
Map 15 C7

Tiniroto Lakes and Community Centre

Tiniroto Rd (SH36), Tiniroto: 36km N of SH38
Lake Falls Hotel Ph (06) 863 7019 www.lakefalls.co.nz

2905900E 6260400N
Hema Atlas Map Ref 21 E6

433
Map 15 C7

Donneraille Park

Along Tiniroto Rd, N of Tiniroto: off SH38 from
S or SH2 from N
Gisborne District Council 'Freedom Camping' Ph (06) 867
2049 www.gdc.govt.nz/Services/FreedomCamping.htm

Freedom Camping is permitted from Labour weekend to Easter; Permit
required — see website for full 'Freedom Camping' details

2908200E 6263800N
Hema Atlas Map Ref 21 E6

SH35 — Opotiki to Gisborne

434
Map 15 A7

Tirohanga Beach Motor Camp

SH35 (Pacific Coast Highway), Tirohanga: E of Opotiki
Ph/Fax (07) 315 7942 tmcamp@xtra.co.nz

Author's note — My pick for the Opotiki area.

2892300E 6348600N
Hema Atlas Map Ref 15 F3

435
Map 15 A7

Opape Motor Camp

7 Opape Rd, Opape: along SH35 NE of Opotiki
Ph (07) 315 8175

Author's note — Simple camping in East Coast style.

2898200E 6349700N
Hema Atlas Map Ref 15 F3

436 — Hawai Bay Camping Ground

Map 15 A7

SH35: Hawai
Ph (07) 315 6308
A caretaker may collect fees if they are in attendance.
Author's note — Just across the road from nice swimming and fishing.

2908900E 6353900N
Hema Atlas Map Ref 15 E4

437 — Te Kaha Holiday Park

Map 13 E7

SH35, Te Kaha
Ph/Fax (07) 325 2894 tekahahp@xtra.co.nz

2924000E 6374200N
Hema Atlas Map Ref 15 C6

438 — Roadside Rest Area

Map 13 E7

Adjacent SH35, Maraetai Bay

2923700E 6375900N
Hema Atlas Map Ref 15 C6

439 — Roadside Rest & Camping Area

Map 13 E7

Adjacent SH35, Waikawa Pt

A caretaker may collect fees if they are in attendance.

2926600E 6380900N
Hema Atlas Map Ref 15 B6

440 — Roadside Rest & Camping Area

Map 13 E7

SH35, Maraehako: just N of Whanarua Bay

A caretaker may collect koha or fees if they are in attendance.
Author's note — The essence of East Coast camping with simple
amenities and beachside with fishing, swimming and canoeing options.
A local Maori family choose to share this magic bay with you, please
respect their generosity.

2933200E 6381400N
Hema Atlas Map Ref 15 B7

441 — Waihau Bay Holiday Park

Map 13 E7

SH35, NE of Waihau Bay: next to the Kowhai Café
Ph (07) 325 3844
Author's note — The beach is just a stroll across the road,
and boat launching is nearby.

2943300E 6387500N
Hema Atlas Map Ref 16 B8

442 — Te Araroa Holiday Park

Map 13 E8

SH35, Te Araroa: W of the township
Ph/Fax (06) 864 4873 bill.martin@xtra.co.nz
Author's note — Nice, quiet and sheltered site even boasting
its own movie theatre.

2980100E 6385800N
Hema Atlas Map Ref 16 B11

443 — Waiapu Caravan Park

Map 15 A8

SH35, at Tikitiki

A caretaker may collect koha or fees if they are in attendance.

2985400E 6364700N
Hema Atlas Map Ref 16 D12

444 Roadside Rest Area

SH35: at turnoff to Ruatoria

Map 15 A8

2976400E 6353700N
Hema Atlas Map Ref 16 E11

445 Waipiro Bay

Kopuaroa Rd from N off SH35 or Waipiro Rd
from S off SH35: Waipiro Bay
Gisborne District Council 'Freedom Camping' Ph (06) 867
2049 www.gdc.govt.nz/Services/FreedomCamping.htm

Map 15 B8

Freedom Camping is permitted from Labour weekend to Easter; Permit
required — see website for full 'Freedom Camping' details

2977100E 6339900N
Hema Atlas Map Ref 16 G11

446 Roadside Rest Area

Adjacent SH35: 7.5km S of Te Puia Springs

Map 15 B8

2973600E 6328900N
Hema Atlas Map Ref 16 H11

447 Waterfront Rest Area

Adjacent SH35: Tokomaru Bay

Map 15 B8

2977000E 6328500N
Hema Atlas Map Ref 16 H11

448 Mayfair Camping Ground

Waitangi St, Tokomaru Bay
Ph (06) 864 5843

Map 15 B8

Author's note — Convenient location near shops and town centre.

2976600E 6327300N
Hema Atlas Map Ref 16 H11

449 Anaura Bay Motor Camp

Anaura Rd: take Anaura turnoff from SH35
N of Tolaga Bay
Ph (06) 862 6380

Map 15 B8

A caretaker may collect koha or fees — if they are in attendance.
Beautiful beach side situation, fishing, boating and swimming
opportunities abound.

2975700E 6315300N
Hema Atlas Map Ref 16 J11

450 Anaura Bay, Waipare Scenic Reserve

Anaura Rd off SH35: 85km N of Gisborne between
Tokomaru Bay and Tolaga Bay
DoC Aniwaniwa Visitor Centre Ph (06) 837 3803
urewerainfo@doc.govt.nz

Map 15 B8

Closed from Easter to Labour Weekend (Oct); boil water from stream;
maximum stay is 3 weeks

2975200E 6318400N
Hema Atlas Map Ref 16 J11

451 Kaiaua Beach

Map 15 B8

Kaiaua Rd, 10km from SH35: signposted about
5km N of Tolaga Bay
Gisborne District Council 'Freedom Camping' Ph (06) 867
2049 www.gdc.govt.nz/Services/FreedomCamping.htm

Freedom Camping is permitted from Labour weekend to Easter;
Permit required – see website for full 'Freedom Camping' details

2976100E 6307200N
Hema Atlas Map Ref 22 A13

452 Roadside Rest Area

Map 15 B8

N side of Uawa River SH35 Bridge

Author's note – Swimming opportunities here.

2973400E 6301300N
Hema Atlas Map Ref 22 A13

453 Tolaga Bay Holiday Park

Map 15 B8

Just off SH35 2km S of Tolaga Bay township:
beside the historic wharf
Ph/Fax (06) 862 6716 tolagabayholidaypark@msn.com
Author's note – Sheltered beach front location.

2973800E 6300100N
Hema Atlas Map Ref 22 A13

454 Loisel's Beach, Waihau Bay

Map 15 B8

Waihau Rd, Waihau Beach: off SH35, about
13km S of Tolaga Bay
Gisborne District Council 'Freedom Camping' Ph (06) 867 2049
www.gdc.govt.nz/Services/FreedomCamping.htm

Freedom Camping is permitted from Labour weekend to Easter;
Permit required – see website for full 'Freedom Camping' details

2971300E 6292800N
Hema Atlas Map Ref 22 B13

455 Pouawa Beach

Map 15 B8

Alongside SH35: right next to the beach
Gisborne District Council 'Freedom Camping' Ph (06) 867
2049 www.gdc.govt.nz/Services/FreedomCamping.htm

Freedom Camping is permitted from Labour weekend to Easter; Permit
required – see website for full 'Freedom Camping' details

2961300E 6273900N
Hema Atlas Map Ref 22 D12

456 Turihaua Beach

Map 15 B8

Alongside SH35: right next to the beach
Gisborne District Council 'Freedom Camping' Ph (06) 867
2049 www.gdc.govt.nz/Services/FreedomCamping.htm

Freedom Camping is permitted from December 26 to February 1;
Permit required – see website for full 'Freedom Camping' details

2959700E 6272600N
Hema Atlas Map Ref 22 D11

457 Tatapouri By the Sea

Map 15 B8

Alongside SH35, Tatapouri
Ph 0800 828 276 info@tatapouri.com
Author's note – This lovely camp was up for sale at the time of re-
search, and its future was in doubt.

2957800E 6270700N
Hema Atlas Map Ref 22 D11

458 Makorori Beach Rest Area

Map 15 B8

Alongside SH35, Makorori Beach

2956300E 6270400N
Hema Atlas Map Ref 22 D11

459 Roadside Rest Area

Okitu Beach, just N of Gisborne

Map 15 B8

2953100E 6268100N
Hema Atlas Map Ref 100 C6, 22 E11

460 Waikanae Beach Holiday Park

Grey St, Gisborne: signposted from city centre
Ph (06) 867 5634 motorcamp@gdc.govt.nz

Author's note — Well run, neat and tidy camp right on the beach and the closest to Gisborne city centre. Also close to boat launching, fun parks and the Aquatic Centre.

Map 15 B8

2946000E 6268800N
Hema Atlas Ref 99 C2, 100 C3, 22 E10

SH2 — Opotiki to Wairoa

461 Roadside Rest Area

Alongside SH2 and the Waioeka river,
Waioeka Gorge Scenic Reserve

Map 15 B7

2883800E 6331200N
Hema Atlas Map Ref 15 G2

462 Roadside Rest Area

Alongside SH2 and the Waioeka river,
Waioeka Gorge Scenic Reserve

Map 15 B7

2889900E 6315200N
Hema Atlas Map Ref 15 J2

463 Manganuku

Adjacent SH2, Waioeka Gorge,
Waioeka Gorge Scenic Reserve
DoC Aniwaniwa Visitor Centre Ph (06) 837 3803
urewerainfo@doc.govt.nz

Self registration system; fishing, walking

Map 15 B7

2894100E 6315000N
Hema Atlas Map Ref 15 J3

464 Whitikau

Takaputahi Rd (access rd unsealed):
Motu Rd off SH2 at Matawai
DoC Aniwaniwa Visitor Centre Ph (06) 837 3803
urewerainfo@doc.govt.nz

Drinking water is from a stream

Map 15 B7

2913000E 6333300N
Hema Atlas Map Ref 15 G5

465 Roadside Rest Areas

On either side of the road, Waioeka Gorge Scenic Reserve

Map 15 B7

2897400E 6309300N
Hema Atlas Map Ref 21 A5

466 Roadside Rest Area

SH2: Papatu Scenic Reserve

Map 15 B7

2909100E 6300700N
Hema Atlas Map Ref 21 A6

467 Roadside Rest Area

SH2, Otoko Walkway Reserve

Map 15 B7

2922600E 6294400N

Hema Atlas Map Ref 22 B8

468 Roadside Rest Area

SH2: near Ormond

Author's note — Shade plus nice vistas of vineyards.

Map 15 B7

2938500E 6290400N

Hema Atlas Map Ref 22 B9

469 Gisborne Showgrounds Park Motorcamp

20 Main Rd, Makaraka: W of Gisborne on SH2
Ph/Fax (06) 867 5299 camp@gisborneshow.co.nz

Map 15 B7

2943600E 6272700N

Hema Atlas Map Ref 100 A2, 22 D10

470 Morere Tea Rooms & Camping Ground

SH2: opposite the Morere Hot Pools
Ph (06) 837 8792 morere@xtra.co.nz

Author's note — Sheltered spot next to a lovely bathing stream, with the hot pools just across the road.

Map 15 C7

2924300E 6235200N

Hema Atlas Map Ref 22 H8

471 Roadside Rest Area

Along Nuhaka Opoutama Rd: S off SH2 towards
Mahia Peninsula

Overnight camping is not allowed

Map 15 C7

2925400E 6227100N

Hema Atlas Map Ref 22 J8

472 Roadside Rest Area

Along Nuhaka Opoutama Rd: S off SH2
towards Mahia Peninsula

Overnight camping is not allowed

Map 15 C7

2927200E 6227100N

Hema Atlas Map Ref 22 J8

473 Mahia Beach Motels & Holiday Camp

43 Moana Dr, Mahia Beach
Ph (06) 837 5830 mahia.beach.motels@xtra.co.nz

Author's note — Beachside spot with beautiful bathing and fishing just across the road, and boat launching facilities close by.

Map 15 C7

2930700E 6224500N

Hema Atlas Map Ref 22 J9

SH2 — Wairoa to Hastings

474 Riverside Motor Camp

Marine Parade, Wairoa: signposted S of bridge
Ph (06) 838 6301 riversidemotorcamp@quicksilver.net.nz

Author's note — Rated Qualmark four stars this park is a little gem, and visiting the toilets is a treat. The river provides good swimming and boating.

Map 15 C7

2891600E 6232100N

Hema Atlas Map Ref 21 H5

475

Map 15 C7

Roadside Rest Area
Beside Wairoa River, S of Wairoa

2889800E 6231900N
Hema Atlas Map Ref 21 H4

476

Map 15 C6

Roadside Rest Area
Adjoining SH2 & the Mohaka River
Great views of the viaducts and river.

2867700E 6229300N
Hema Atlas Map Ref 21 J2

477

Map 15 C6

Waikare River
Waikare Rd: from SH2 at Putorino turn onto Waikare Rd,
then follow the unsealed road for approximately 20min
to the road end
DoC Napier Information Centre Ph (06) 834 3111
napier-ao@doc.govt.nz
Fishing, swimming, boating

2859500E 6217200N
Hema Atlas Map Ref 28 A13

478

Map 15 C6

Roadside Rest Area
Adjacent SH2 & Lake Tutira

2846400E 6212700N
Hema Atlas Map Ref 28 A12

479

Map 15 C6

Lake Tutira, Hawke's Bay
Adjacent SH2, Tutira
DoC Napier Information Centre Ph (06) 834 3111
napier-ao@doc.govt.nz
Fishing, swimming, boating (no motorised craft)

2847600E 6212700N
Hema Atlas Map Ref 28 A12

480

Map 15 C6

Roadside Rest Area
Adjacent SH2, White Pine Bush Scenic Reserve

2844100E 6206700N
Hema Atlas Map Ref 28 B12

481

Map 15 C6

Waipatiki Beach Farm Park
Waipatiki Beach Rd, Waipatiki Beach: Tangoio Rd
off SH2, then Waipatiki Rd
Ph (06) 836 6075 waipatiki@xtra.co.nz

2853600E 6204700N
Hema Atlas Map Ref 28 B13

482

Map 15 C6

Eskdale Caravan Park
Yule Rd, Eskdale: signposted 4km N from SH5 and
SH2 intersection
Ph/Fax (06) 836 6864
Author's note — Very peaceful, shaded and sheltered spot on the
banks of the Esk River, yet only 20 minutes from Napier town centre.

2840700E 6195000N
Hema Atlas Map Ref 28 C12

483

Map 15 C6

Glenfalls, Mohaka River

From SH5 turn into Waitara Rd, follow the unsealed
road for approximately 10min
DoC Napier Information Centre Ph (06) 834 3111
napier-ao@doc.govt.nz

Drinking water is from a stream; fishing, swimming, canoeing, rafting

2828200E 6222000N

Hema Atlas Map Ref 20 J10

484

Map 15 C6

Everetts, Mohaka River

From SH5 turn into Waitara Rd, follow the unsealed
road for approximately 20min, turn into Auroa Rd
and follow to sign
DoC Napier Information Centre Ph (06) 834 3111
napier-ao@doc.govt.nz

Drinking water is from a stream; fishing, swimming, canoeing, rafting

2831300E 6228000N

Hema Atlas Map Ref 20 J11

485

Map 15 C6

Mangatutu Hot Springs, Kaweka Forest Park

From Puketitiri Rd turn right into Pakaututu Rd then
left into Makahu Rd, follow to the road end (access rd
unsealed with river ford)
DoC Napier Information Centre Ph (06) 834 3111
napier-ao@doc.govt.nz

Drinking water is from a stream; fishing, swimming, tramping

2808100E 6218000N

Hema Atlas Map Ref 28 A8

486

Map 15 C6

Bay View Snapper Holiday Park

10 Gill Rd, Bay View: between the beach & SH2, N of Napier
Ph (06) 836 7084 or 0800 287 275 www.snapperpark.co.nz

Author's note — Qualmark four star rated park in a sheltered,
water's edge location.

2843900E 6190100N

Hema Atlas Map Ref 28 C12

487

Map 15 C6

Bay View Van Park

Cnr SH2 & Onehunga Rd, Bay View: N of Napier
Ph/Fax (06) 836 6064 bayviewvanpark@paradise.net.nz

Author's note — The park has brand new facilities that are exclusively
available to motorhomes, campervans and caravans. No camping, and
not much shade either at the moment.

2842200E 6189600N

Hema Atlas Map Ref 28 D12

488

Map 15 D6

Westshore Holiday Park

88 Meeanee Quay, Westshore Napier: signposted
off SH2 N of Napier
Ph/Fax (06) 835 9456 westshoreholiday@xtra.co.nz

Author's note — Neat and tidy park close to the beach and an
inlet with a wildlife reserve.

2844400E 6185400N

Hema Atlas Map Ref 103 B1, 28 D12

489

Map 15 D6

Kennedy Park Top 10 Holiday Park

11 Storkey St, Napier: signposted from SH2 & SH50
S of Napier
Ph 0800 457 275 info@kennedypark.co.nz

Author's note — Set in park-like grounds and handy to Napier
centre, this park is rated four star by Qualmark.

2845300E 6181700N

Hema Atlas Map Ref 103 B1, 28 D12

490

Map 15 D6

Roadside Rest Area

Several rest areas N of this vicinity between SH2
and the beachfront

Author's note — This site at the mouth of the Ngaruroro River
is favoured by anglers.

2846100E 6175300N

Hema Atlas Map Ref 103 A3, 28 E12

491

Map 15 D6

Clive Motor Camp

31 Farndon Rd, Clive: signposted from SH2,
N of Clive River
Ph (06) 870 0609

2845300E 6173300N

Hema Atlas Map Ref 103 A4, 28 E12

492

Map 15 D6

Beachside Rest Area

Clifton Rd: beachside en route to Clifton

Author's note — Tents and caravans are not permitted, but campervans
are allowed to stay two nights for free.

2850500E 6169200N

Hema Atlas Map Ref 103 A5, 28 F13

493

Map 15 D6

Te Awanga Park Holiday Park

52 Kuku Street, Te Awanga: signposted N from Clifton Rd
Ph/Fax (06) 875 0334

Author's note — Right next to the beach for swimming and surfing.

2852300E 6167700N

Hema Atlas Map Ref 28 F13

494

Map 15 D6

Clifton Beach Reserve Motor Camp

Clifton Rd, Clifton
Ph/Fax (06) 875 0263

Author's note — Magic location, and you can walk to the gannet colony.

2853500E 6167000N

Hema Atlas Map Ref 28 F13

495

Map 15 D6

Raceview Motel & Holiday Park

307 Gascoigne St, Hastings: signposted off SH2
at S end of Hastings
Ph/Fax (06) 878 8837 raceview@xtra.co.nz.
Author's note — About three star rating, adjoining the racecourse.

2838300E 6166400N

Hema Atlas Map Ref 103 C5, 28 F11

496

Map 15 D6

Hastings Top 10 Motor Camp

610 Windsor St, Hastings: signposted off Heretunga St,
en route to Havelock North
Freephone 0508 427 846 www.hastingsholidaypark.co.nz
holidaypark@hastingstourism.co.nz

Author's note — Top 10's usual high standard (four star plus
Qualmark rating) and handy to Splash Planet and a picturesque park.

2841200E 6165400N

Hema Atlas Map Ref 103 C5, 28 F12

497

Map 15 D6

Arataki Motels & Holiday Park

139 Arataki Rd, Havelock North: hard to find from the
S but signposted from the Napier to Havelock Rd
Ph/Fax (06) 877 7479 arataki.motel.holiday.park@xtra.co.nz
Author's note — The Arataki Honey Centre is just up the road.

2845300E 6165100N

Hema Atlas Map Ref 103 B6, 28 F12

498 Ocean Beach Camping Ground

Map 15 D6

Ocean Beach Rd, Ocean Beach: off Waimarama Rd
from Havelock North

A caretaker may collect fees if they are in attendance.
Author's note — Handy to a great beach for surfing and fishing.

2854100E 6155400N
Hema Atlas Map Ref 28 G13

499 Waimarama Seaside Resort

Map 15 D6

30 Harper St, Waimarama: visible from the main
road as you enter Waimarama
Ph (06) 874 6813

Author's note — Handy to a magic beach. Although the camp
could do with more development it meets all the basic requirements.

2851900E 6147600N
Hema Atlas Map Ref 28 H13

LOWER NORTH REGION

Mount Taranaki

SH1 — Wellington to SH3

500 Wahine Bay

Map 17 B6

Breaker Bay Rd, Breaker Bay, Wellington

Author's note — Picturesque parking and picnicking just kilometres from
central Wellington and the ferries.

2663000E 5983000N
Hema Atlas Map Ref 110 E2, 33 F2

501 Karaka & Scorching Bay Reserves

Map 17 B6

Karaka Bay Rd, Seatoun Bays, Wellington

Author's note — Picturesque parking and picnicking just kilometres
from central Wellington and the ferries.

2663800E 5987800N
Hema Atlas Map Ref 110 E2, 33 F2

502 Picnic Reserves

Map 17 B6

Shelly Bay Road & Massey Rd, Maupuia, Wellington

Author's note — Picturesque parking and picnicking just kilometres
from central Wellington and the ferries.

2661900E 5988900N
Hema Atlas Map Ref 110 E2, 33 F2

503

Map 17 B6

Capital Gateway Motor Lodge & Caravan Park

1 Newlands Rd, Newlands, Wellington
Ph (04) 478 7812 or 0800 996 996
capitalgateway@xtra.co.nz

Author's note — Functional, but not very pretty, this is the closest supervised campervan camp to the ferry terminal. It's suitable for campervans and big rigs but not for tent camping.

2662300E 5995800N
Hema Atlas Map Ref 110 C2, 33 E2

504

Map 17 B6

Camp Elsdon

18 Raiha St, Porirua: 23km NW of Wellington, off SH1
Ph (04) 237 8987 camp_elsdon@xtra.co.nz

Author's note — Functional but not pretty, and not suited to big rigs.

2662800E 6006300N
Hema Atlas Map Ref 110 B2, 33 D2

505

Map 17 B6

Murton's Motor Camp

3 Whitford Brown Ave, Porirua: follow signs NW
of Porirua from the Titahi Bay Road
Ph (04) 235 9599 or info@murtons.co.nz

2666500E 6007200N
Hema Atlas Map Ref 110 B3, 33 D2

506

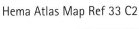

Map 17 A6

Motukaraka Point Reserve

East of SH1 at Plimmerton on minor road linking to SH58

Author's note — Sheltered site with nice views of Pauatahanui Inlet.

2668800E 6010800N
Hema Atlas Map Ref 33 C2

507

Map 17 A6

Roadside Rest Area

QE2 Park, Paekakariki: signposted W of SH1

2674400E 6024300N
Hema Atlas Map Ref 33 B3

508

Map 17 A6

Paekakariki Holiday Park

180 Wellington Rd, Paekakariki: signposted W of SH1
Ph/Fax (04) 292 8292 paekakariki.holiday.park@xtra.co.nz

Author's note — This gem of a camp is a nice surprise. It's located within QE2 park with nice walks to the beach, good facilities and plenty of space.

2675700E 6024300N
Hema Atlas Map Ref 33 B3

509

Map 14 E4

Lindale Motor Park

Ventnor Drive, Paraparaumu: W of SH1, 1km N of
Paraparaumu
Ph/Fax (04) 298 8046 lindalemotorpark@xtra.co.nz

2679300E 6031800N
Hema Atlas Map Ref 33 A3

510

Map 14 E4

Kapiti Holiday Resort

16 Beach Haven Place, Paraparaumu Beach
Ph (04) 233 1965

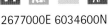

2677000E 6034600N
Hema Atlas Map Ref 33 A3

511
Map 14 E4

El Rancho

Kauri Rd, Waikanae: signposted W of SH1

Caretaker will collect fees.
Author's note — A strange name for a Christian camp but this
site welcomes all. It has good facilites in park-like surrounds and
is extremely peaceful.

2680800E 6035500N
Hema Atlas Map Ref 33 A4

512
Map 14 E4

Otaki Forks

14km E of Otaki, on Otaki Gorge Rd, Tararua Forest Park
DoC Wellington Conservation Information Centre
Ph (04) 472 7356 wellingtonvc@doc.govt.nz
Fire ban applies all year

2698900E 6035200N
Hema Atlas Map Ref 33 A5

513
Map 14 E4

Bridge Lodge

3 Otaki Gorge Rd, Otaki: signposted off SH1
just S of the Otaki River bridge
Ph (06) 364 6667 bridge.lodge@xtra.co.nz
Author's note — Handy to Tararua Forest Park, and located
beside a nice river.

2691400E 6045200N
Hema Atlas Map Ref 33 J4

514
Map 14 E4

Roadside Rest Area

Alongside SH1: S of Otaki

2691700E 6046400N
Hema Atlas Map Ref 33 J4

515
Map 14 E4

Byron's Resort

20 Tasman St, Otaki Beach: signposted W of SH1 at Otaki
Ph 0800 800 122 www.byronsresort.co.nz byrons.
resort@xtra.co.nz
Author's note — Nice camp that's tidy and sheltered.

2688300E 6049400N
Hema Atlas Map Ref 33 J3

516
Map 14 E4

Roadside Rest Area

Otaki Beach: W of SH1

Author's note — Waterside picnic area.

2688200E 6050700N
Hema Atlas Map Ref 33 H3

517
Map 14 E4

Roadside Rest Area

Alongside SH1: approx 2km N of Otaki

2693500E 6050300N
Hema Atlas Map Ref 33 H4

518
Map 14 E4

Waikawa

9km north of Otaki, on North Manakau Rd,
Tararua Forest Park
DoC Wellington Conservation Information Centre
Ph (04) 472 7356 wellingtonvc@doc.govt.nz

2700300E 6051300N
Hema Atlas Map Ref 33 H5

519

Map 14 E4

Tatum Park

W side of SH1: midway between Levin & Otaki
Ph (06) 362 6799 bookings@tatumpark.co.nz

Author's note — Great facilities in a sheltered location that is handy to Wellington. This former Boy Scouts' camp is now available to all.

2697800E 6055100N
Hema Atlas Map Ref 33 H4

520

Map 14 E4

Levin Motorcamp

38 Parker Ave, Levin: signposted from SH57 & SH1
Ph (06) 368 3549 info@levinmotorcamp.co.nz

2703700E 6061500N
Hema Atlas Map Ref 33 G5

521

Map 14 E4

Roadside Rest Area

E of SH1: on N edge of Levin

2704700E 6062800N
Hema Atlas Map Ref 33 G5

522

Map 14 E4

Roadside Rest Area

SH57: S of Shannon

2711200E 6068000N
Hema Atlas Map Ref 33 G6

523

Map 14 E4

Hydrabad Holiday Park

Forest Rd, Waitarere Beach: signposted on entry into the township
Ph (06) 368 4941 hydrabad@paradise.net.nz

Author's note — Neat and tidy park.

2696300E 6069800N
Hema Atlas Map Ref 33 G4

524

Map 14 E4

Waitarere Beach Motor Camp

133 Park Ave, Waitarere Beach
Ph (06) 368 8732 wbmc@paradise.net.nz

Author's note — Next to the beach.

2697200E 6071500N
Hema Atlas Map Ref 33 F4

525

Map 14 E4

Roadside Rest Area

SH1: on the S bank of the Manawatu River

2702100E 6074200N
Hema Atlas Map Ref 33 F5

526

Map 14 E4

Foxton Beach Motor Camp

Holben Parade, Foxton Beach: off SH1 at Foxton
Ph (06) 363 8211

Author's note — This site is handy to the beach, with a children's playground and tennis courts. The Manawatu Caravan Club offer a second motor camp in the area if needed.

2698000E 6079800N
Hema Atlas Map Ref 33 F4

527

Map 14 E4

Roadside Rest Area

SH1: N of Foxton

2703800E 6082000N
Hema Atlas Map Ref 33 E5

528

Map 14 E4

Roadside Rest Area

SH1: N of Foxton

Author's note — The roadside roosters are a bit a novelty here.

2706200E 6084500N
Hema Atlas Map Ref 33 E5

529

Map 14 E4

Himatangi Motor Camp

35 Koputara Rd, Himatangi Beach: off SH1 at Himatangi
Ph (06) 329 9575 himatangicamp@actrix.co.nz

Author's note — New owners are breathing fresh life into this nice wee camp.

2699900E 6091100N
Hema Atlas Map Ref 33 D4

530

Map 14 E4

Roadside Rest Area

Adjacent SH1: N of SH56 intersection

2707900E 6094200N
Hema Atlas Map Ref 33 D5

531

Map 14 E4

Tangimoana Motor Camp

Koura St, Tangimoana: Rosina Rd off SH1, then Tangimoana Rd, at give way sign in town centre turn right into Punga St, then left into Koura St

A caretaker may collect fees if they are in attendance.

2700400E 6099100N
Hema Atlas Map Ref 33 D5

SH1 — From SH3 to Waiouru

532

Map 14 D4

Marton Camping Grounds

Maunder St, Marton: off Signal St, signposted at N end of town

A caretaker may collect fees if they are in attendance.
Author's note — A nice wee spot with established trees in sheltered location next to the town's gardens.

2712400E 6124500N
Hema Atlas Map Ref 29 A6

533

Map 15 D5

Roadside Rest & Camping Area

Adjacent SH1, Queens Park, Hunterville: E of SH1 at N end of Hunterville

Author's note — No facilities other than shade, shelter and picnic tables but it's a nice spot right next to SH1 and handy to Hunterville's restaurants and cafes.

2730400E 6138400N
Hema Atlas Map Ref 26 J13

534

Map 15 D5

Vinegar Hill (Putai Ngahere Reserve)

Putai Ngahere Reserve: near junction of SH1 & SH54

2734100E 6138100N
Hema Atlas Map Ref 27 J1

535

Map 15 D5

Roadside Rest Area

Makohine Viaduct, W of SH1

2739500E 6145400N
Hema Atlas Map Ref 27 H1

536

Map 15 D5

Roadside Rest Area

Just N of Makohine Viaduct, E of SH1

2741200E 6144400N
Hema Atlas Map Ref 27 H2

Author's note — Splendid views of the Rangitikei River.

537

Map 15 D5

Mangaweka Camping Grounds

1km E of SH1, Mangaweka
Mangaweka Adventure Company
Ph (06) 382 5744 www.rra.co.nz

Author's note — Sheltered and tranquil spot in a magic location
with boating, canoeing, rafting and swimming options nearby.

2750300E 6150700N
Hema Atlas Map Ref 27 G3

538

Map 15 D5

Roadside Rest Area

Adjacent SH1: N of Mangaweka & S of Taihape

2748900E 6156100N
Hema Atlas Map Ref 27 G2

539

Map 15 D5

Roadside Rest Area

Adjacent SH1: approximately 8km S of Taihape

2753800E 6158300N
Hema Atlas Map Ref 27 G3

540

Map 15 D5

Taihape River View Holiday Park

Old Abattoir Rd, Taihape: 3km N of Taihape off SH1
Ph/Fax (06) 388 0718
taihape.riverview.holidaypark@xtra.co.nz

Author's note — Don't be put off by the industrial area nearby.

2749300E 6168700N
Hema Atlas Map Ref 27 F2

541

Map 15 D5

Roadside Rest Area

Adjacent SH1 and the Hautapu River: NW of Taihape

2746800E 6170400N
Hema Atlas Map Ref 27 E2

542

Map 15 D5

Roadside Rest Area

Titoki Point: E of SH1

2741400E 6181700N
Hema Atlas Map Ref 27 D2

543

Map 15 D5

Roadside Rest Area

Rangitikei River Bridge Reserve, Taihape-Napier Road

2770300E 6187000N
Hema Atlas Map Ref 27 D5

Author's note — Waterside picnic area.

544

Map 15 C5

Roadside Rest Area

Taruarau River Bridge Reserve, Taihape-Napier Road

2787700E 6192500N
Hema Atlas Map Ref 27 C6

Author's note — Waterside picnic area.

545

Map 15 C5

Ngaruroro, Kaweka Forest Park

Kaweka Forest Park, Taihape-Napier Road
DoC Napier Information Centre Ph (06) 834 3111
napier-ao@doc.govt.nz
Author's note — Informal camping area with nice fishing spot nearby.

2796300E 6196500N
Hema Atlas Map Ref 27 C7

546

Map 15 C5

Cameron, Kaweka Forest Park

Adjacent Taihape-Napier Rd, near Kuripapango
DoC Napier Information Centre Ph (06) 834 3111
napier-ao@doc.govt.nz
Drinking water is from stream; tramping, fishing, canoeing

2796500E 6197700N
Hema Atlas Map Ref 27 C7

547

Map 15 C6

Lawrence, Kaweka Forest Park

From Napier-Taihape Rd turn into Lawrence Rd,
follow to the road end (access rd unsealed)
DoC Napier Information Centre Ph (06) 834 3111
napier-ao@doc.govt.nz
Drinking water is from a stream; tramping, fishing, swimming

2805000E 6192900N
Hema Atlas Map Ref 28 C8

SH2 — Wellington to Masterton

548

Map 17 B6

Top 10 Hutt Park Holiday Park

95 Hutt Park Rd, Lower Hutt: turnoff at roundabout
at E end of Petone Esplanade
Ph (04) 568 5913 or 0800 488 872 info@huttpark.co.nz
Author's note — Handy to both Wellington and the Hutt Valley and an
ideal spot to await, or recover from, a Cook Strait ferry crossing.

2670300E 5995300N
Hema Atlas Map Ref 110 D3, 33 E3

549

Map 17 B6

Catchpool Valley, Rimutaka Forest Park

Coast Rd, 10km S of Wainuiomata
DoC Wellington Conservation Information Centre
Ph (04) 472 7356 wellingtonvc@doc.govt.nz
Gates open 8am to dusk.
Author's note — A pretty setting with a safe stream for paddling yet
only one hour from downtown Wellington.

2670100E 5981200N
Hema Atlas Map Ref 33 F2

550

Map 17 B6

Roadside Rest Area

SH2: S of Upper Hutt, alongside the Hutt River

2681400E 6008600N
Hema Atlas Map Ref 33 D4

551

Map 17 A6

Harcourt Holiday Park

45 Akatarawa Rd, Upper Hutt: 4km N of Upper Hutt,
signposted from SH2
Ph (04) 526 7400 www.harcourtholidaypark.co.nz
hacourtholidaypark@xtra.co.nz
Author's note — Plenty of shade and shelter, and adjoining
a major park with established trees and gardens.

2686300E 6010500N
Hema Atlas Map Ref 33 C4

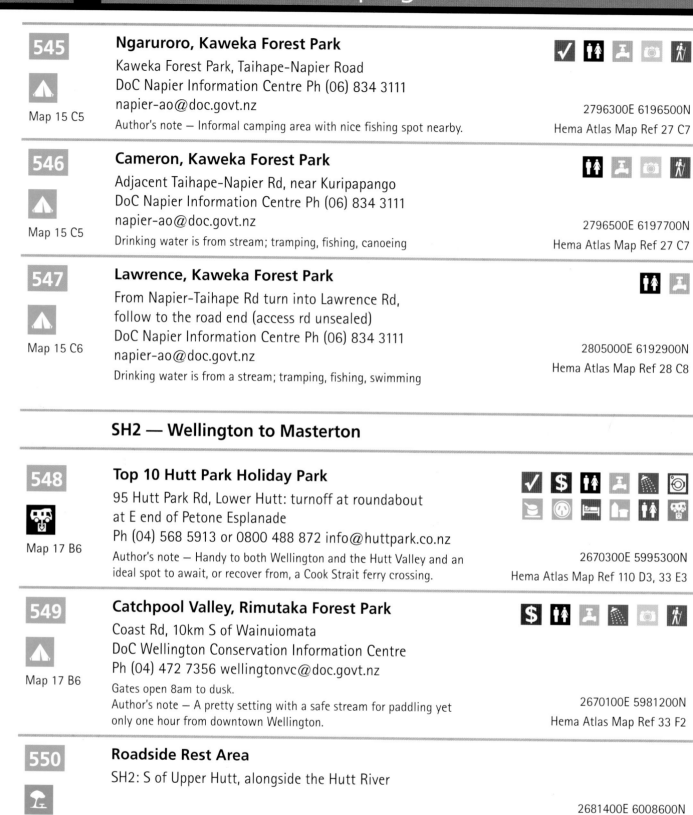

552

Map 17 B7

Rimutaka Summit Rest Area
SH2, Rimutaka Forest Park: 555m above sea level

2697400E 6008600N
Hema Atlas Map Ref 33 D5

553

Map 17 B7

Roadside Rest Area
SH2: E side of Rimutakas, near Featherston

2704600E 6008700N
Hema Atlas Map Ref 33 D6

554

Map 17 B7

Roadside Rest Area
SH53: alongside Ruamahanga River, NW of Martinborough

Author's note — Swimming and picnicking spot.

2715300E 5998500N
Hema Atlas Map Ref 34 E7

555

Map 17 B7

Martinborough Village Camping Ground
Cnr Princes & Dublin Sts, Martinborough:
signposted from SH53 on E side of town
Ph (06) 306 8919
A caretaker may collect fees if they are in attendance.
Author's note — Located right beside Martinborough's swimming pool.

2715100E 5996100N
Hema Atlas Map Ref 34 E7

556

Map 17 B6

Lake Ferry Holiday Park
Lake Ferry: SE of Martinborough along Martinborough Lake
Ferry Rd, adjoining main road
Ph (06) 307 7873 lakeferry@wise.net.nz
Author's note — Situated on the shores of Lake Onoke with swimming
and boating at your back door.

2688600E 5977900N
Hema Atlas Map Ref 33 G4

557

Map 17 B7

Pinnacles, Putangirua Pinnacles Scenic Reserve
Whatarangi Rd, Putangirua Pinnacles Scenic Reserve:
off Lake Ferry Rd
DoC Wellington Conservation Information Centre
Ph (04) 472 7356 wellingtonvc@doc.govt.nz
Drinking water is from a stream

2696300E 5971200N
Hema Atlas Map Ref 33 G5

558

Map 17 B7

Roadside Rest Area
W of SH2, S end of Greytown

Author's note — Nice sheltered garden for a picnic.

2715200E 6010900N
Hema Atlas Map Ref 34 C7

559

Map 17 A7

Greytown Memorial Park Camping Ground
Memorial Park, Kuratawhiti St, Greytown: W of SH2,
N end of town
Custodian Ph (06) 304 9837
A caretaker may collect fees if they are in attendance.

2716300E 6012200N
Hema Atlas Map Ref 34 C7

560 Waiohine Gorge, Tararua Forest Park

Map 17 A7

Waiohine Gorge Rd, Tararua Forest Park: Swamp Rd off SH2,
then Moffats Rd, then Josephs Rd, then Waiohine Gorge Rd;
18km NW of Greytown
DoC Wellington Conservation Information Centre
Ph (04) 472 7356 wellingtonvc@doc.govt.nz

2711900E 6020600N
Hema Atlas Map Ref 33 B7

561 Carterton Holiday Park

Map 17 A7

198 Belvedere Rd, Carterton: W of SH2, N end of town
Ph (06) 378 6454 cartertonholidaypark@contact.net.nz

2721700E 6018300N
Hema Atlas Map Ref 34 C8

562 Holdsworth, Tararua Forest Park

Map 17 A7

Mt Holdsworth Rd, Tararua Forest Park: Norfolk Rd off SH2
at Waingawa, then left into Mt Holdsworth Rd;
15km W of Masterton
DoC Wellington Conservation Information Centre
Ph (04) 472 7356 wellingtonvc@doc.govt.nz

2719200E 6029800N
Hema Atlas Map Ref 34 B7

563 Mawley Park Motor Camp

Map 17 A7

15 Oxford St, Masterton: N of bridge W of SH2
at N end of town
Ph/Fax (06) 378 6454 jclarke@contact.net.nz

Author's note — A popular camp that is nice and handy to
a major swimming complex, QE2 Park, gardens and play areas.

2734000E 6026400N
Hema Atlas Map Ref 34 B9

564 Riversdale Beach Holiday Park

Map 17 A8

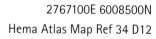

Riversdale Beach Rd, Riversdale Beach: take Masterton
Castlepoint Rd to Carswell, then Blairlogie Langdale Rd,
then Homewood Rd, then Riversdale Beach Rd; on the right
of the main road as you enter Riversdale
Ph/Fax (06) 372 3889 holidaypark@inspire.net.nz

2767100E 6008500N
Hema Atlas Map Ref 34 D12

565 Castlepoint Holiday Park

Map 17 A8

Jetty Rd, Castlepoint: follow Masterton Castlepoint Rd from
Masterton to Castlepoint; beachside E of main road at N
end of Castlepoint
Ph (06) 372 6705 holiday@castlepoint.co.nz

Author's note — Simple camping in a stunning beachside location, with
surfing, boating and fishing at your doorstep.

2781700E 6030100N
Hema Atlas Map Ref 34 A13

SH2 — Masterton to Dannevirke

566 Roadside Rest Area

Map 15 E5

W of SH2: N of Masterton

2731300E 6036200N
Hema Atlas Map Ref 34 A9

567

Map 15 E5

Roadside Rest Area

E of SH2: N of Masterton

2732200E 6039100N
Hema Atlas Map Ref 34 A9

568

Map 15 E4

Kiriwhakapapa, Tararua Forest Park

End of Kiriwhakapapa Rd, Tararua Forest Park:
turn off SH2 16km N of Masterton
DoC Wellington Conservation Information Centre
Ph (04) 472 7356 wellingtonvc@doc.govt.nz

2724300E 6040300N
Hema Atlas Map Ref 34 A8

569

Map 15 E5

Miller's Reserve Roadside Rest Area

W of SH2: N of Mt Bruce National Wildlife Centre, 8.5km S
of Eketahuna

2733900E 6052900N
Hema Atlas Map Ref 31 H2

570

Map 15 E5

Eketahuna Camping

Stout St, Eketahuna: off SH2 at Bridge St,
into Stanley St, into Stout St
Ph 025 816 460

A caretaker may collect fees if they are in attendance.
Author's note — A simple, but nice, camp in a lovely riverside location.

2737900E 6058200N
Hema Atlas Map Ref 31 H2

571

Map 15 E5

Alfredton Domain Rest Area

Alfredton Rd (SH52), Alfredton: E of SH2 at Eketahuna
Alfredton Domain Board Ph (06) 375 8440

Overnight camping allowed; donation appreciated

2750900E 6055200N
Hema Atlas Map Ref 31 G3

572

Map 15 E5

Roadside Rest Area

Adjacent SH2: N of Eketahuna

2741800E 6069400N
Hema Atlas Map Ref 31 F3

573

Map 15 E5

Roadside Rest Area

Adjacent SH2: S of Pahiatua

2749900E 6077300N
Hema Atlas Map Ref 31 F3

574

Map 15 E5

Carnival Park Campground

Glasgow St, Pahiatua: Halls Rd off SH2, then turn
left into Glasgow St; 1km W of SH2 at S end of Pahiatua
Ph (06) 376 6340

Author's note — An unexpected gem set in five acres of park.

2749400E 6079400N
Hema Atlas Map Ref 31 F3

575

Map 15 E5

Woodville Domain Camping Area

Signposted from SH2 at N end of town, E of SH2

Author's note — A bit public and austere.

2754100E 6091800N
Hema Atlas Map Ref 31 D4

576

Map 15 E5

Ashhurst Domain

Ashhurst Domain, Ashhurst: cnr of SH3 and Cambridge Ave

A caretaker may collect fees if they are in attendance.

2744800E 6097400N
Hema Atlas Map Ref 31 D3

577

Map 15 D5

Totara Reserve/Camp Rangi Woods

Pohangina Valley East Rd, Totara Reserve
Ph (06) 326 9310 (after hours)

2753200E 6116400N
Hema Atlas Map Ref 31 B4

578

Map 15 E5

Roadside Rest Area

Adjacent SH2, S side: 2km N of Woodville

2756000E 6091600N
Hema Atlas Map Ref 31 D4

579

Map 15 E5

Coppermine, Ruahine Forest Park

From SH2 at Woodville turn into Pinfold Rd,
then Coppermine Rd, follow to the road end
DoC Napier Information Centre Ph (06) 834 3111
napier-ao@doc.govt.nz
Tramping

2757300E 6102900N
Hema Atlas Map Ref 31 C4

580

Map 15 D5

Kumeti, Ruahine Forest Park

From SH2 west of Dannevirke turn into Umatoaroa Rd,
then left into Top Grass Rd, then right into Tamaki West rd,
follow to the road end
DoC Napier Information Centre Ph (06) 834 3111
napier-ao@doc.govt.nz
Drinking water is from a stream; tramping

2764300E 6110900N
Hema Atlas Map Ref 31 B5

581

Map 15 D5

Tamaki West, Ruahine Forest Park

From SH2 west of Dannevirke turn into Umatoaroa Rd,
then left into Top Grass Rd, then right into Tamaki West rd,
follow to the road end
DoC Napier Information Centre Ph (06) 834 3111
napier-ao@doc.govt.nz
Drinking water is from a stream; tramping

2769000E 6116500N
Hema Atlas Map Ref 31 B5

582

Map 15 E5

Dannevirke Holiday Park

29 George St, Dannevirke: signposted at N end of town,
E of SH2
Ph/Fax (06) 374 7625 dannevirkeholidaypark@xtra.co.nz
Author's note — Simple, but nice, park set in sheltered park-like grounds
next to a scenic reserve with lots of ducks and wildlife for the children.

2775100E 6105800N
Hema Atlas Map Ref 31 C6

583

Map 15 E5

Akitio Beach Camping Ground

Akitio Beach: Weber Rd from Dannevirke, then Route 52 to
Waione, then River Rd to Akitio; 1 hour east of Dannevirke
Ph (06) 374 3450

2798300E 6061100N
Hema Atlas Map Ref 32 G8

584

Map 15 E6

Herbertville Motor Camp

10 Seaview Rd, Herbertville: Weber Rd from Dannevirke,
then Route 52 from Weber to Wimbledon, then Herbertville
Rd to Herbertville; 68km east of Dannevirke
Ph (06) 374 3446

2810600E 6073500N
Hema Atlas Map Ref 32 F10

SH2 — Dannevirke to Hastings

585

Map 15 D5

Roadside Rest Area

E of SH2: N of Dannevirke

2778200E 6110300N
Hema Atlas Map Ref 31 B6

586

Map 15 D5

Roadside Rest Area With Camping

ANZAC Park, adjacent SH2 4km N of Norsewood

Casual camping allowed.
Author's note — Shaded and sheltered, with access to a pretty stream.

2784400E 6122600N
Hema Atlas Map Ref 31 A7

587

Map 15 D6

Tikokino Camping Ground

Adjoining Sawyers Arms Hotel & Café, SH50, Tikokino:
27km N of SH2 junction (N of Norsewood)
Sawyers Arms Hotel Ph (06) 856 5881

2805500E 6149100N
Hema Atlas Map Ref 31 A7

588

Map 15 D5

Takapau NZMCA Camp

Takapau: off SH2 13km N of Norsewood or
21km S of Waipukurau; from Takapau town centre
follow NZMCA signs
www.nzmca.org.nz
A caretaker may collect fees if they are in attendance. Author's note
— Best suited to caravans and mobile campers.

2794900E 6125600N
Hema Atlas Map Ref 32 A8

589

Map 15 D6

Roadside Rest Area

Adjoining SH2: W of Waipukurau

2806000E 6130400N
Hema Atlas Map Ref 32 A9

590

Map 15 D6

Waipukurau Holiday Park

River Tce, Waipukurau: adjoining SH2, N end of town, next
to Tukituki River
Ph (06) 858 8184

2813100E 6129400N
Hema Atlas Map Ref 32 A10

591

Map 15 E6

Beach Road Holiday Park

566 Beach Rd, Porangahau Beach: Porangahau Rd from SH2
at Waipukurau
Ph (06) 855 5281

2820800E 6093100N
Hema Atlas Map Ref 32 D11

592 Te Paerahi Beach

Map 15 E6

Cnr Te Paerahi St & Puketauhinu Pl, Porangahau: Porangahau Rd from SH2 at Waipukurau
Central Hawke's Bay District Council 'Freedom Camping'
(06) 857 8060

Casual campers must notify the Council's Bylaw Officer of their name, address and contact telephone number as well as their intended camp spot and length of stay.

2822000E 6094500N
Hema Atlas Map Ref 32 D11

593 Blackhead Beach Camping Ground

Map 15 E6

McHardy Pl, Blackhead Beach: from Waipukurau take Farm Rd, then Motere Rd, then Long Range Rd; or from Waipawa take Pourerere Rd, then Long Range Rd
Ph (06) 857 7335

2836400E 6108400N
Hema Atlas Map Ref 32 C12

594 River's Edge Holiday Park

Map 15 D6

Hawke St, Waipawa: adjoining SH2, S end of town
Ph/Fax (06) 857 8976 paddy.mccloskey@paradise.net.nz
Author's note — Next to Waipawa's Centennial Swimming Pool and the Waipawa River.

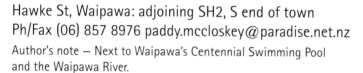

2817200E 6133500N
Hema Atlas Map Ref 28 J9

595 Pourerere Beach

Map 15 D6

Pourerere Rd, Pourerere Beach: take Pourerere Rd from Waipawa
Central Hawke's Bay District Council 'Freedom Camping'
(06) 857 8060

Casual campers must notify the Council's Bylaw Officer of their name, address and contact telephone number as well as their intended camp spot and length of stay.

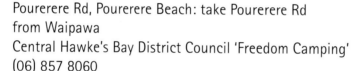

2840500E 6115500N
Hema Atlas Map Ref 32 B13

596 Kairakau Beach

Map 15 D6

N end of Beach Rd, Kairakau Beach: from Waipawa take Pourerere Rd, then River Rd, then Elsthorpe Rd then Kairakau Rd
Central Hawke's Bay District Council 'Freedom Camping' (06) 857 8060

Casual campers must notify the Council's Bylaw Officer of their name, address and contact telephone number as well as their intended camp spot and length of stay.

2846200E 6133100N
Hema Atlas Map Ref 28 J12

SH3 — Palmerston North to Wanganui

597 Palmerston North Holiday Park

Map 15 E5

133 Dittmer Drive, Palmerston North: signposted off Fitzherbert St East
Ph/Fax (06) 358 0349
www.holidayparks.co.nz/palmerstonnorth
Author's note — Close to the aquatic centre for swimming, Victoria Esplanade Gardens and the Manawatu River.

2731400E 6089300N
Hema Atlas Map Ref 105 C3, 30 E8

598

Map 15 E5

Feilding Holiday Park

5 Arnott St, Feilding: N side of Feilding, signposted off Kimbolton Rd

Ph/Fax (06) 323 5623 feildingholidaypark@hotmail.com

Author's note — Sheltered park in well-established grounds.

2730200E 6107900N

Hema Atlas Map Ref 29 C7

599

Map 14 D4

Bridge Motorhome Park

2 Bridge St, Bulls: E end of Bulls

Ph 0800 27 43 43 bullsmotel@infogen.net.nz

Author's note — Sheltered riverside location.

2714100E 6110800N

Hema Atlas Map Ref 29 B6

600

Map 14 D4

Duddings Lake Motorcamp & Picnic Park

1525 Bulls/Turakina Hwy (SH3): signposted approx 19km W of Bulls

Ph (06) 327 8127 duddingslake@clear.net.nz

Author's note — A fabulous location for a family break with good facilities and sheltered with its own small lake.

2703700E 6120400N

Hema Atlas Map Ref 29 A5

601

Map 14 D4

Roadside Rest Area

S of SH3: S of Wanganui Rd to Marton

2698600E 6125000N

Hema Atlas Map Ref 29 A4

602

Map 14 D4

Koitiata Camping Ground

Turakina Beach Rd, Kotiata: signposted S of SH3, E of Turakina Valley Rd intersection

A caretaker may collect fees if they are in attendance.
Author's note — Compact, clean and tidy spot with access to the beach across the road.

2691800E 6124300N

Hema Atlas Map Ref 29 A4

603

Map 14 D4

Wiritoa Lake Reserve Rest Area

Kaitake Rd: signposted approx 6km E of Wanganui off SH3

Author's note — Lakeside picnic spot, with opportunities for boating, swimming and canoeing.

2687700E 6135000N

Hema Atlas Map Ref 26 J8

604

Map 14 D4

Scoutlands

316 Kaitake Rd: further along from the Wiritoa Lake Reserve

Ph (06) 348 8648

Author's note — Lakeside camping spot, that is sheltered and quiet, yet close to Wanganui.

2688000E 6133800N

Hema Atlas Map Ref 26 J8

605

Map 14 D4

Bignell St Motel & Caravan Park

18 Bignell St, Wanganui: follow the signs to Castlecliff from SH3, at E side of Wanganui

Ph 0800 244 635 info@bignellstreetmotel.co.nz

Author's note — Budget camping and long-stay permanent accommodation.

2682500E 6138700N

Hema Atlas Map Ref 109 D3, 26 J8

606 Avro Motel & Caravan Park

Map 14 D4

36 Alma Rd, Wanganui: S of the racecourse
Ph 0800 367 287
bookings@wanganuiaccommodation.co.nz
Author's note — The handiest to the city centre. Each powered site has its own toilet and shower, which is a nice touch.

2683700E 6138900N
Hema Atlas Map Ref 109 C3, 26 J8

607 Castlecliff Seaside Holiday Park

Map 14 D4

19 Rangiora St, Castlecliff: signposted S of Wanganui off SH3 at Eastern entrance to Wanganui
Ph 0800 254 947 tokiwipark@xtra.co.nz
Author's note — Seaside 'Wanganui style': you have to go through an industrial area to get there, but the camp is good and tidy.

2679300E 6139200N
Hema Atlas Map Ref 109 C1, 25 J7

SH4 — Wanganui to Ohakune

608 Aramoho Hotel & Caravan Park

Map 14 D4

181 Somme Pde, Wanganui
Ph (06) 343 8340
Author's note — A modern variation of the traditional paddock beside a hotel. It was hot, dry and dusty when we visited and probably more suited to permanent campers.

2685300E 6142900N
Hema Atlas Map Ref 109 A5, 26 H8

609 Wanganui River Top 10 Holiday Park

Map 14 D4

160 Somme Pde, Upper Aramoho, Wanganui: just follow the W bank of the river inland 5km
Ph 0800 27 26 64 wrivertop10@xtra.co.nz
Author's note — Sheltered and shady park backing onto the river for swimming and boating.

2688500E 6144400N
Hema Atlas Map Ref 109 A6, 26 H8

610 Roadside Rest Area

Map 14 D4

Between SH4 and Whanganui River: N of Wanganui

2688700E 6143100N
Hema Atlas Map Ref 109 A6, 26 H8

611 Roadside Rest Area

Map 14 D4

Adjacent Whanganui River Rd at the summit of Aromoana: about 2km N of SH4

Author's note — Extensive views of the Whanganui River Valley from this point.

2692500E 6151400N
Hema Atlas Map Ref 26 G9

612 Roadside Rest & Camping Area

Map 14 D4

Adjacent Whanganui River Rd: about 23km N of SH4

Casual camping permitted

2692300E 6161500N
Hema Atlas Map Ref 26 F9

613

Map 14 D4

Kauika Campsite

Adjacent Whanganui River Rd:
about 45km N of SH4 or 16km S of Pipiriki
Caretaker, Winiata Tapa Ph (06) 342 8762

Fees payable to Caretaker.
Author's note — Clean and tidy site: better than some serviced holiday parks! A good base if you are wanting to spend more time in this area.

2691800E 6178900N
Hema Atlas Map Ref 26 E9

614

Map 14 D4

Jerusalem Rest Area

Adjacent Whanganui River Rd, Jerusalem:
about 50km N of SH4 or 11km S of Pipiriki

2688300E 6182400N
Hema Atlas Map Ref 26 D8

615

Map 14 C4

Pipiriki Rest Area

Adjacent Whanganui River Rd, Pipiriki: about 25km from SH4 at Raetihi

2685300E 6190600N
Hema Atlas Map Ref 26 C8

616

Map 14 C4

Raetihi Holiday Park

10 Parapara Rd, Raetihi
Ph (06) 385 4176

Author's note — Clean and functional.

2707400E 6194100N
Hema Atlas Map Ref 26 C10

SH3 — Wanganui to Hawera

617

Map 14 D4

Mowhanau Camp

Kai Iwi Beach: 5km S of SH3 from just W of Kai Iwi
Ph/Fax (06) 342 9658 campwhanau@hotmail.com

Author's note — Just back from the beach, in a very pretty setting.

2672300E 6145900N
Hema Atlas Map Ref 25 H7

618

Map 14 D4

Ashley Park

Adjacent SH3: 15 min N of Wanganui
Ph (06) 346 5917 www.ashleypark.co.nz

The owner will collect fees. Author's note — Suprisingly nice farmstay accommodation for campers and mobile campers.

2661500E 6154600N
Hema Atlas Map Ref 25 G6

619

Map 14 D4

Nukumaru Recreation Reserve

Waiinu Beach: signposted from SH3, follow
Waiinu Beach Rd from Waitotara
Ph (06) 346 5938

A donation is expected. Author's note — Right beside the beach, but could be a tad exposed if it is windy.

2658600E 6147600N
Hema Atlas Map Ref 25 H5

620

Map 14 D3

Waverley Beach Domain

Waverley Beach Rd: 9km S of SH3 at Waverley
Ph 0800 111 323 or 025 278 3586 for bookings

A caretaker may collect koha or fees if they are in attendance.

2649400E 6151000N
Hema Atlas Map Ref 25 G4

621

Map 14 D3

Carlyle Beach Motor Camp

9 Beach Rd, Patea: signposted at the E end of Patea
at the top of the hill; 1km S of Patea where the Patea River
meets the sea
Ph (06) 273 8620

A caretaker may collect koha or fees if they are in attendance.

2636800E 6158400N
Hema Atlas Map Ref 25 G3

622

Map 14 D3

Roadside Rest Area

Adjacent SH3: about 17km W of Patea

2627400E 6173100N
Hema Atlas Map Ref 25 E2

SH45 — Hawera to New Plymouth

623

Map 14 D3

Ohawe Beach Motor Camp

Rangatapu Street, Ohawe: 9km S of SH45
Ph (06) 278 6939

A caretaker may collect koha or fees if they are in attendance.
Author's note — Simple beachside camping.

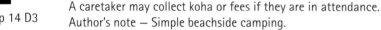

2612200E 6179100N
Hema Atlas Map Ref 23 H6

624

Map 14 D3

**Kaupokonui Recreation Reserve
& Camping Ground**

Lower Glenn Road, Kaupokonui: S of SH45
just E of Kaupokonui
Ph (06) 274 8577

Author's note — Simple camping at a quiet beachside haven, with
good fishing and surfing at your door step. It's one of the best spots
south of Mt Taranaki.

2601800E 6182200N
Hema Atlas Map Ref 23 G5

625

Map 14 C3

Opunake Beach Holiday Park

Beach Rd, Opunake: signposted from the centre of Opunake
Ph (06) 761 7525 0800 758 009 opunakebeach@xtra.co.nz

Author's note — Well worth checking out because it is right next to the
beach with playgrounds for the children, and not far from good surf.

2583400E 6193400N
Hema Atlas Map Ref 23 F3

626

Map 14 C3

Roadside Rest Area

Adjacent SH45 at Pungarehu: near the Cape Egmont & Pari-
haka turnoffs

2580500E 6213500N
Hema Atlas Map Ref 23 D3

627

Map 14 C2

Roadside Rest Area

Seaside at the end of Cape Road: W of SH45
from Pungarehu

2574700E 6214800N
Hema Atlas Map Ref 23 D2

628

Map 14 C3

Oakura Beach Holiday Park

2 Jans Tce, Oakura: signposted N of SH45,
15km W of New Plymouth
Ph (06) 752 7861 oakurabeachcamp@internet.co.nz
Author's note — Surfside camping at this favoured surf haunt.

2591400E 6231200N
Hema Atlas Map Ref 23 B4

629

Map 14 C3

Belt Road Seaside Holiday Park

2 Belt Rd, New Plymouth: signposted N of SH45,
W of city centre
Ph 0800 804 204 www.beltroad.co.nz info@beltroad.co.nz
Author's note — Although this is the closest camp to the town centre,
it's beachside and you feel miles away. The coastal walkway makes
the walk to town a pleasure.

2601300E 6238300N
Hema Atlas Map Ref 107 B3, 23 B5

630

Map 14 C3

Aaron Court Motels & Holiday Park

119 Junction Road (SH3), New Plymouth:
S of New Plymouth city centre
Ph 0800 101 939
www.aaroncourt.net.nz aaron.court@infogen.net.nz

2604200E 6235000N
Hema Atlas Map Ref 107 C5, 23 B5

631

Map 14 C3

Hookner Park

885 Carrington Rd, Hurworth: approx 5 km S of New Plymouth city centre
Ph (06) 753 9506 or (06) 753 6945
Author's note — Peaceful rural environment.

2602400E 6230800N
Hema Atlas Map Ref 23 B5

SH3 & SH43 — Hawera to Taumarunui

632

Map 14 D3

King Edward Park Motor Camp

Adjacent SH3: N of Hawera
Ph/Fax (06) 278 8544 www.holidayparks.co.nz/kingedward
Author's note — A handy base from which to visit the nearby
Tawhiti Museum.

2620000E 6179700N
Hema Atlas Map Ref 25 E2

633

Map 14 C3

Roadside Rest Area

Alongside SH3: S of Stratford

Author's note — Nice views of Mt Egmont (Mt Taranaki).

2622600E 6203300N
Hema Atlas Map Ref 25 B2

634

Map 14 C3

Stratford Top 10 Holiday Park

410 Page St, Stratford: W of SH3 signposted
S of the town centre
Ph 0508 478 728 stratfordholpark@hotmail.com
Author's note — Shaded and sheltered site in spacious grounds.
Handy to Stratford's parks and swimming pool.

2620000E 6206400N
Hema Atlas Map Ref 25 B1

635 Roadside Rest Area

SH43 (Forgotten World Hwy): E of Stratford

Map 14 C3   Author's note – Hilltop views of Mt Egmont (Mt Taranaki).

2639300E 6212400N
Hema Atlas Map Ref 25 A3

636 Te Wera Forest Camp

SH43 (Forgotten World Hwy): E of Stratford

Self registration system or a caretaker will collect modest fees.
Map 14 C3   Author's note – Simple sheltered camping.

2648600E 6217600N
Hema Atlas Map Ref 25 A4

637 Whangamomona

SH43 (Forgotten World Hwy): 64km from SH3 at Stratford;
campsite occupies the old school grounds, 500m S of the
township, signposted by the hotel
Map 14 C4   Enquire at the Whangamomona Hotel Ph (06) 762 5823

2660700E 6226700N
Hema Atlas Map Ref 17 J6

638 Kaieto Cafe & Caravan Park

SH43 (Forgotten World Hwy): midway between
Stratford & Taumarunui
Ph (06) 762 5858 kaietocafe@bitworks.co.nz
Map 14 C4   Author's note – Small hilltop campsite with impressive
views plus a cafe.

2666700E 6236300N
Hema Atlas Map Ref 17 H6

639 Roadside Rest Area

SH43 at the Tangarakau River Bridge: Morgans Grave,
Tangarakau Scenic Reserve

Map 14 C4   Author's note – Take the walk to some nice swimming holes.

2669600E 6246500N
Hema Atlas Map Ref 17 G6

640 Ohinepane

SH43 (Wanganui River Rd): 21km from Taumarunui
DoC Whanganui Area Office Ph (06) 348 8475

Map 14 C4   Self registration system or a caretaker will collect the modest fees.

2695000E 6249100N
Hema Atlas Map Ref 18 G9

641 Roadside Rest Area

SH43 (Wanganui River Rd): alongside the Whanganui River

Map 14 C4

2703400E 6251100N
Hema Atlas Map Ref 18 F10

NELSON & MARLBOROUGH REGION

Kayaking, Abel Tasman National Park.

Queen Charlotte Drive - Picton to SH6

642

Map 17 B5

Picton Campervan Park

25 Oxford St, Picton: signposted en route between
ferry terminals and SH1
Ph (03) 573 8875 picton.cvpark@xtra.co.nz

Author's note - The handiest camp to the town centre and
ferry terminals.

2595000E 5990500N

Hema Atlas Ref 113 D2, 114 C3, 40 G10

643

Map 17 B5

Picton Top 10 Holiday Park

70-78 Waikawa Rd, Picton: follow the signs towards
Waikawa Bay from Picton town centre
Ph 0800 277 444 enquiries@pictontop10.co.nz

Author's note - Clean, quiet and sheltered: all you expect from Top 10,
and there are not many camps that can earn a five star Qualmark
rating. Handy to boat launching facilities and the marina.

2595000E 5990500N

Hema Atlas Ref 113 B5, 114 C3, 40 G10

644

Map 17 B5

Alexanders Holiday Park

Canterbury St, Picton
Ph/Fax (03) 573 6378

2595000E 5990500N

Hema Atlas Ref 113 D3, 114 D3, 40 G10

645

Map 17 B5

Parklands Marina Holiday Park

10 Beach Rd, Waikawa Bay
Ph/Fax (03) 573 6343 parktostay@xtra.co.nz

Author's note - Handy to boat launching facilities.

2596000E 5992900N

Hema Atlas Map Ref 114 B4, 40 G10

646

Map 17 B5

Waikawa Bay Holiday Park

5 Waimarama St, Waikawa Bay
Ph (03) 573 7434 hiyah@ihug.co.nz

Author's note - Handy to boat launching facilities.

2597200E 5993200N

Hema Atlas Map Ref 114 B5, 40 G10

647

Map 17 B5

Whatamango Bay, Queen Charlotte Sound

Port Underwood Rd, Queen Charlotte Sound:
off SH6, N of Renwick
www.doc.govt.nz or Picton Visitor Information Centre
Ph (03) 520 3113 pivc@destinationmarlborough.com

2601100E 5993000N

Hema Atlas Map Ref 40 G11

648

Map 17 B5

Governors Bay Scenic Reserve

Seaside, on Queen Charlotte Drive: W of Picton

2590800E 5992900N
Hema Atlas Map Ref 114 A1, 40 G10

649

Map 17 B5

Ngakuna Bay Rest Area

Seaside, on Queen Charlotte Drive: W of Picton

Author's note - A Motor Caravan Association private camp at the east end of town, and a harbourside rest area at the west end of town.

2590800E 5992900N
Hema Atlas Map Ref 40 G10

650

Map 17 B5

Momorangi Bay Holiday Park, Queen Charlotte Sound

Momorangi Bay, Grove Arm, Queen Charlotte Sound
(road and boat access)
www.doc.govt.nz or Picton Visitor Information Centre
Ph (03) 520 3113 pivc@destinationmarlborough.com
Bookings Ph (03) 573 7865

2588600E 5993100N
Hema Atlas Map Ref 40 G9

651

Map 17 B5

Aussie Bay, Queen Charlotte Sound

Near Momorangi Bay, on Queen Charlotte Drive
(road and boat access)
www.doc.govt.nz or Picton Visitor Information Centre
Ph (03) 520 3113 pivc@destinationmarlborough.com
Author's note - Simply beautiful.

2587400E 5992700N
Hema Atlas Map Ref 40 G9

652

Map 17 B5

Roadside Rest Area

Anakiwa, start of the Queen Charlotte Walkway:
off Queen Charlotte Drive

2587100E 5993900N
Hema Atlas Map Ref 40 G9

653

Map 17 B5

Davies Bay, Queen Charlotte Sound

Grove Arm, Queen Charlotte Sound (access via
Queen Charlotte Walkway and boat only)
www.doc.govt.nz or Picton Visitor Information Centre
Ph (03) 520 3113 pivc@destinationmarlborough.com

2588200E 5994900N
Hema Atlas Map Ref 40 G9

654

Map 17 B5

Smiths Farm Holiday Park

Adjacent Queen Charlotte Drive: 13km E of Havelock
Ph (03) 574 2806 cbfaulls@xtra.co.nz

Author's note - Tidy and clean, but limited summer shade.

2584100E 5991100N
Hema Atlas Map Ref 40 G9

655

Map 17 B5

Roadside Rest Area

Seaside, on Queen Charlotte Drive: E of Havelock

2578400E 5991100N
Hema Atlas Map Ref 40 G8

656

Map 17 B5

Cullen Point Lookout

Seaside, on Queen Charlotte Drive: E of Havelock

2575800E 5993400N

Hema Atlas Map Ref 40 G8

657

Map 17 B5

Havelock Motor Camp

24 Inglis St, Havelock: NE of SH6
Ph (03) 574 2329
Author's note - Conveniently located between the town
and boat harbour.

2574500E 5992700N

Hema Atlas Map Ref 40 G8

658

Map 17 B5

Chartridge Park Holiday Camp

Adjacent SH6: 7km S of Havelock
Ph (03) 574 2129

2574900E 5985000N

Hema Atlas Map Ref 40 H8

659

Map 17 B5

Moutapu Bay, Pelorus Sound

Moutapu Bay, Mahau Sound (road and boat access)
DoC Nelson Regional Visitor Centre Ph (03) 546 9339
nelsonvc@doc.govt.nz

2581300E 5994400N

Hema Atlas Map Ref 40 G9

660

Map 17 B5

Roadside Rest Area

Ohingaroa DoC Reserve, Mahau Sound:
N of Queen Charlotte Drive

2583700E 5995700N

Hema Atlas Map Ref 40 G9

661

Map 17 B5

Putanui Point, Pelorus Sound

Putanui Point, Pelorus Sound (boat access only)
DoC Nelson Regional Visitor Centre Ph (03) 546 9339
nelsonvc@doc.govt.nz

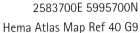

2582700E 5997400N

Hema Atlas Map Ref 40 G9

662

Map 17 B5

Cowshed Bay, Pelorus Sound

Portage Rd, Kenepuru Sound (road and boat access)
DoC Nelson Regional Visitor Centre Ph (03) 546 9339
nelsonvc@doc.govt.nz
Author's note - A small waterside camp spot that is more suitable for
campers and small vans. Big rigs and caravans could find this road tricky.

2596000E 5999200N

Hema Atlas Map Ref 40 G10

663

Map 17 B5

Picnic Bay, Pelorus Sound

Picnic Bay, Kenepuru Sound (road and boat access)
DoC Nelson Regional Visitor Centre Ph (03) 546 9339
nelsonvc@doc.govt.nz

2597500E 6001300N

Hema Atlas Map Ref 40 F10

664

Map 17 B5

Nikau Cove, Pelorus Sound

Picnic Bay, Kenepuru Sound (road and boat access)
DoC Nelson Regional Visitor Centre Ph (03) 546 9339
nelsonvc@doc.govt.nz

2597500E 6001300N

Hema Atlas Map Ref 40 F10

665 Black Rock, Queen Charlotte Sound

Map 17 B5

Queen Charlotte Walkway (access via walking
track and boat only)
www.doc.govt.nz or Picton Visitor Information Centre
Ph (03) 520 3113 pivc@destinationmarlborough.com

2599200E 6000100N
Hema Atlas Map Ref 40 F10

666 Kumutoto Bay, Queen Charlotte Sound

Map 17 B5

Queen Charlotte Sound (boat access only)
www.doc.govt.nz or Picton Visitor Information Centre
Ph (03) 520 3113 pivc@destinationmarlborough.com

2600600E 5999100N
Hema Atlas Map Ref 40 G11

667 Ratimera Bay, Queen Charlotte Sound

Map 17 B5

Ratimera Bay, Queen Charlotte Sound (boat access only)
www.doc.govt.nz or Picton Visitor Information Centre
Ph (03) 520 3113 pivc@destinationmarlborough.com

2603000E 5999600N
Hema Atlas Map Ref 40 G11

668 Bay of Many Coves Saddle,
Queen Charlotte Sound

Map 17 B5

Queen Charlotte Walkway (access via walking
track and boat only)
www.doc.govt.nz or Picton Visitor Information Centre
Ph (03) 520 3113 pivc@destinationmarlborough.com

2606600E 6003600N
Hema Atlas Map Ref 40 F11

669 Blumine Island, Queen Charlotte Sound

Map 17 B5

Queen Charlotte Sound (boat access only)
www.doc.govt.nz or Picton Visitor Information Centre
Ph (03) 520 3113 pivc@destinationmarlborough.com

2614100E 6003100N
Hema Atlas Map Ref 40 F12

670 Ngaruru Bay, Queen Charlotte Sound

Map 17 B5

Ngaruru Bay, Tory Channel (boat access only)
www.doc.govt.nz or Picton Visitor Information Centre
Ph (03) 520 3113 pivc@destinationmarlborough.com

2611600E 5997800N
Hema Atlas Map Ref 40 G12

671 Wharehunga Bay, Queen Charlotte Sound

Map 17 B6

Wharehunga Bay, Queen Charlotte Sound (boat access only)
www.doc.govt.nz or Picton Visitor Information Centre
Ph (03) 520 3113 pivc@destinationmarlborough.com

2618600E 6001700N
Hema Atlas Map Ref 40 F12

672 Kenepuru Head, Pelorus Sound

Map 17 B5

Kenepuru Sound Rd: head of Kenepuru Sound
(road and boat access)
DoC Nelson Regional Visitor Centre
Ph (03) 546 9339 nelsonvc@doc.govt.nz
Author's note - Access not suited to big rigs and caravans.

2603300E 6004800N
Hema Atlas Map Ref 40 F11

673

Map 17 B5

Ferndale, Pelorus Sound

Kenepuru Sound (boat access only)
DoC Nelson Regional Visitor Centre Ph (03) 546 9339
nelsonvc@doc.govt.nz

2591700E 6001700N
Hema Atlas Map Ref 40 F10

674

Map 17 A5

Waimaru, Pelorus Sound

Kenepuru Sound Rd, Waimaru Bay, outer Pelorus Sound
DoC Nelson Regional Visitor Centre Ph (03) 546 9339
nelsonvc@doc.govt.na
Author's note - Access not suited to big rigs and caravans.

2596700E 6014700N
Hema Atlas Map Ref 40 E10

675

Map 17 B5

Camp Bay, Queen Charlotte Sound

Endeavour Inlet, Queen Charlotte Sound (access via Queen
Charlotte Walkway and boat only)
www.doc.govt.nz or Picton Visitor Information Centre
Ph (03) 520 3113 pivc@destinationmarlborough.com

2606400E 6008700N
Hema Atlas Map Ref 40 F11

676

Map 17 B5

School House Bay, Queen Charlotte Sound

Resolution Bay, Queen Charlotte Sound (access only via
Queen Charlotte Walkway and boat)
www.doc.govt.nz or Picton Visitor Information Centre
Ph (03) 520 3113 pivc@destinationmarlborough.com

2613500E 6009700N
Hema Atlas Map Ref 40 F12

677

Map 17 A5

Cannibal Cove, Queen Charlotte Sound

Outer Queen Charlotte Sound (boat access only)
www.doc.govt.nz or Picton Visitor Information Centre
Ph (03) 520 3113 pivc@destinationmarlborough.com

2614800E 6014300N
Hema Atlas Map Ref 40 E12

SH6 - Havelock to Richmond

678

Map 17 B5

The Trout Hotel

SH6, Canvastown
Ph (03) 574 2888

2565200E 5992100N
Hema Atlas Map Ref 39 G7

679

Map 17 B5

Pinedale Motor Camp

820 Wakamarina Road, Canvastown: 9km S of SH6 from
Canvastown
Ph (03) 574 2349 pinedale.motor.camp@xtra.co.nz
Open October to April

2562500E 5984100N
Hema Atlas Map Ref 39 H7

680

Map 17 B5

Butchers Flat, Mt Richmond Conservation Park

End of Waikamarina Rd, Waikamarina Valley:
off SH6 at Canvastown
DoC Nelson Regional Visitor Centre Ph (03) 546 9339
nelsonvc@doc.govt.nz

2559300E 5981100N
Hema Atlas Map Ref 39 H6

681 Pelorus Bridge

Map 17 B5

Adjacent SH6: 19km NW of Havelock
www.doc.govt.nz or Picton Visitor Information Centre
Ph (03) 520 3113 pivc@destinationmarlborough.com
Bookings Ph (03) 571 6019

Author's note - This site has magic swimming holes and walks, but remember to bring the insect repellant.

2557300E 5987600N
Hema Atlas Map Ref 39 H6

682 Roadside Rest Area

Map 17 B5

Alfred Stream, adjacent SH6: at S end
of Rai Valley township

2557900E 5997300N
Hema Atlas Map Ref 39 G6

683 Roadside Rest Area

Map 17 B5

Carluke DoC Reserve, off SH6
DoC Visitor Information centre - Ph (03) 520 3113
pivc@destinationmarlborough.com
No camping allowed.

2559300E 5999600N
Hema Atlas Map Ref 39 G6

684 Roadside Rest Area

Map 17 B5

Brown River Picnic Area, SH6: at the turnoff
to Tennyson Inlet

2559300E 5999600N
Hema Atlas Map Ref 39 G6

685 Roadside Rest Area

Map 17 B5

Tennyson Inlet DoC Reserve: 43km NE of Rai Valley
DoC Visitor Information centre - Ph (03) 520 3113
pivc@destinationmarlborough.com

Author's note - This route is not suited to caravans and big rigs.

2572000E 6007500N
Hema Atlas Map Ref 39 F8

686 Harvey Bay, Pelorus Sound

Map 17 A5

Harvey Bay, Tennyson Inlet: 43km NE of Rai Valley
DoC Nelson Regional Visitor Centre Ph (03) 546 9339
nelsonvc@doc.govt.nz

Author's note - This peaceful spot is located in a sheltered valley and set back from the water. However, this route is not recommended for big rigs and caravans.

2571900E 6009900N
Hema Atlas Map Ref 40 E8

687 Duncan Bay, Pelorus Sound

Map 17 A5

Duncan Bay, Tennyson Inlet: 43km NE of Rai Valley
DoC Nelson Regional Visitor Centre Ph (03) 546 9339
nelsonvc@doc.govt.nz

Author's note - This route is not suited to caravans and big rigs.

2574500E 6010300N
Hema Atlas Map Ref 40 E8

688 Ngawhakawhiti, Pelorus Sound

Map 17 A5

Tennyson Inlet, Pelorus Sound (walking track
and boat access only)
DoC Nelson Regional Visitor Centre Ph (03) 546 9339
nelsonvc@doc.govt.nz
Stream water only

2576200E 6009900N
Hema Atlas Map Ref 40 E8

689

🏕
Map 17 B5

Nydia, Pelorus Sound

Nydia Bay, Pelorus Sound (boat access only)
DoC Nelson Regional Visitor Centre Ph (03) 546 9339
nelsonvc@doc.govt.nz

2574600E 6005200N
Hema Atlas Map Ref 40 F8

690

🏕
Map 17 B5

Pipi Beach, Pelorus Sound

Hikapau Reach, Pelorus Sound (boat access only)
DoC Nelson Regional Visitor Centre Ph (03) 546 9339
nelsonvc@doc.govt.nz

2581900E 6003100N
Hema Atlas Map Ref 40 F9

691

🏕
Map 17 B5

Jacobs Bay, Pelorus Sound

Dillon Bell Point, Pelorus Sound (boat access only)
DoC Nelson Regional Visitor Centre Ph (03) 546 9339
nelsonvc@doc.govt.nz

2583600E 6009700N
Hema Atlas Map Ref 40 F9

692

🏕
Map 17 A5

Tawa Bay, Pelorus Sound

Tawa Bay, Tennyson Inlet (boat access only)
DoC Nelson Regional Visitor Centre Ph (03) 546 9339
nelsonvc@doc.govt.nz

2579900E 6014800N
Hema Atlas Map Ref 40 F8

693

🏕
Map 17 A5

Kauauroa, Pelorus Sound

Outer Pelorus Sound (boat access only)
DoC Nelson Regional Visitor Centre Ph (03) 546 9339
nelsonvc@doc.govt.nz
Stream water only

2591100E 6018200N
Hema Atlas Map Ref 40 E10

694

🚐
Map 17 A5

Okiwi Bay Holiday Park

Okiwi Bay: 22km N of Rai Valley, Ronga Rd N from SH6
Ph (03) 576 5006 info@okiwi.co.nz

Author's note - This is a nice small camp, but it has limited
facilities (three toilets and three showers) so it could get crowded
at peak holiday times.

2565500E 6011000N
Hema Atlas Map Ref 39 E7

695

🏕
Map 17 A5

Elaine Bay, Pelorus Sound

French Pass Rd, Elaine Bay, Tennyson Inlet
(road and boat access)
DoC Nelson Regional Visitor Centre Ph (03) 546 9339
nelsonvc@doc.govt.nz

2575300E 6017100N
Hema Atlas Map Ref 40 E8

696

🏕
Map 17 A5

Waiona Bay, Pelorus Sound

Outer Pelorus Sound (boat access only)
DoC Nelson Regional Visitor Centre Ph (03) 546 9339
nelsonvc@doc.govt.nz
Stream water only

2583700E 6023000N
Hema Atlas Map Ref 40 D9

697 French Pass, Pelorus Sound

Road end of Croiselles/French Pass Rd, French Pass
(road and boat access)
DoC Nelson Regional Visitor Centre Ph (03) 546 9339
nelsonvc@doc.govt.nz

Map 17 A5

2581600E 6030200N
Hema Atlas Map Ref 40 C9

698 Lucky Bay, D'Urville Island

Lucky Bay, East Coast D'Urville Island (boat access only)
DoC Nelson Regional Visitor Centre Ph (03) 546 9339
nelsonvc@doc.govt.nz
Stream water only

Map 14 E3
17 A5

2582900E 6035300N
Hema Atlas Map Ref 40 C9

699 Penguin Bay, D'Urville Island

Penguin Bay, East Coast D'Urville Island (boat access only)
DoC Nelson Regional Visitor Centre Ph (03) 546 9339
nelsonvc@doc.govt.nz
Stream water only

Map 14 E3
17 A5

2586700E 6040600N
Hema Atlas Map Ref 40 B9

700 Mill Arm, D'Urville Island

Mill Arm, Greville Harbour, D'Urville Island
(boat access only)
DoC Nelson Regional Visitor Centre Ph (03) 546 9339
nelsonvc@doc.govt.nz
Stream water only

Map 14 E3
17 A5

2580300E 6040900N
Hema Atlas Map Ref 40 B9

701 South Arm, D'Urville Island

South Arm, Port Hardy, D'Urville Island (boat access only)
DoC Nelson Regional Visitor Centre Ph (03) 546 9339
nelsonvc@doc.govt.nz
Stream water only

Map 14 E3
17 A5

2582400E 6043800N
Hema Atlas Map Ref 40 B9

702 Rene Cove, D'Urville Island

Rene Cove, Port Hardy, D'Urville Island (boat access only)
DoC Nelson Regional Visitor Centre Ph (03) 546 9339
nelsonvc@doc.govt.nz
Stream water only

Map 14 E3
17 A5

2582900E 6045500N
Hema Atlas Map Ref 40 B9

703 Roadside Rest Area

Collins Valley Picnic Area, adjacent SH6: NW of Rai Valley

Map 17 B5

2556200E 6002900N
Hema Atlas Map Ref 39 F6

704 Roadside Rest Area

Adjacent SH6, alongside the Collins River: NW of Rai Valley

Map 17 B5

2553700E 6005700N
Hema Atlas Map Ref 39 F6

705

Map 17 B5

Roadside Rest Area
Adjacent SH6, Graham Stream: NW of Rai Valley

2550300E 6002900N
Hema Atlas Map Ref 39 F6

706

Map 17 B5

Roadside Rest Area
Adjacent SH6, Hira Forest: NE of Nelson

2544300E 5998600N
Hema Atlas Map Ref 39 G5

707

Map 16 B4

Cable Bay Holiday Park
Cable Bay: 9km N of SH6, 23km E of Nelson
Ph (03) 545 0003 cablebayfarm@tasman.net
Author's note - Small, sheltered, seaside camp, with good fishing and walking, yet only 23km from Nelson.

2543900E 6004600N
Hema Atlas Map Ref 39 F5

708

Map 16 B4

Roadside Rest Area
Cable Bay: 9km N of SH6, 23km E of Nelson

2544300E 6005800N
Hema Atlas Map Ref 39 F5

709

Map 16 B4

Roadside Rest Area
Nelson Botanic Gardens, Nelson

2535300E 5992600N
Hema Atlas Ref 115 C6, 116 A5, 39 G4

710

Map 16 B4

Matai Valley Motor Camp
472 Matai Valley Rd, Nelson: 8km SE of the city centre
Ph/Fax (03) 548 7729
Author's note - Sheltered and spacious camp set in native bush and adjoining a swimming stream - yet only eight minutes drive from downtown Nelson.

2536500E 5990900N
Hema Atlas Map Ref 116 B6, 39 G4

711

Map 16 B4

Brook Valley Holiday Park
584A Brook St, Brook Valley: S of Matai Valley & Nelson
Ph (03) 548 0399

2533900E 5989500N
Hema Atlas Map Ref 116 C5, 39 H4

712

Map 16 B4

Nelson City Holiday Park
230 Vanguard St, Nelson: S of Nelson city centre, head S on Rutherford St and into Waimea Rd
Ph 0800 77 88 98 info@nelsonholidaypark.co.nz
Author's note - The handiest camp to the city centre.

2532300E 5991500N
Hema Atlas Map Ref 116 B4, 39 G4

713

Map 16 B4

Tahuna Beach Holiday Park

70 Beach Rd, Tahunanui: signposted at the W end
of Rocks Rd, where it meets Tahunanui Beach
Ph (03) 348 5159 tahunabeach.co.nz

Author's note - A huge and popular camp handy to the city,
yet right on the beach.

2529800E 5991400N

Hema Atlas Map Ref 116 B4, 39 G3

SH60 - Richmond to Collingwood

714

Map 16 B4

Richmond Motel & Top 10 Holiday Park

29 Gladstone Rd (SH6), Richmond: 1km S of Richmond
Ph 0800 250 218 richmondmotel@xtra.co.nz

2524600E 5986100N

Hema Atlas Map Ref 116 D2, 39 H3

715

Map 16 B4

Club Waimea, Waimea Town & Country Club

343 Queen St, Richmond: just W of the
SH6 intersection with Queen St

2524600E 5986100N

Hema Atlas Map Ref 116 C2, 39 H3

716

Map 16 B4

Greenwood Park Caravan Park

Cnr Landsdowne Rd & Appleby Highway, Appleby
Ph (03) 544 4685 greenwood.park@xtra.co.nz

Author's note - Handy to seasonal fruit picking opportunities.

2522100E 5988400N

Hema Atlas Map Ref 116 C1, 39 H3

717

Map 16 B4

Roadside Rest Area

SH60: W of the Appleby Bridge on the Waimea River

Author's note - This spot provides nice swimming and
picnic opportunities.

2521100E 5989500N

Hema Atlas Map Ref 116 C1, 39 H3

718

Map 16 B4

Mapua Leisure Park

33 Toru St, Mapua: follow the signs to the centre
of Mapua from SH60
Ph (03) 540 2666 leisure-park@mapua.gen.nz

Author's note - Magic sheltered setting with 'clothes optional'
bathing for those who dare.

2518400E 5995800N

Hema Atlas Map Ref 39 G2

719

Map 16 B4

Roadside Rest Area

Several spots adjacent SH60 at Ruby Bay:
W of Motueka, N of Richmond

2517800E 5997500N

Hema Atlas Map Ref 39 G2

720

Map 16 B4

McKee Memorial Reserve

Seaside at the W end of Ruby Bay: signposted from SH60

A caretaker may collect fees if they are in attendance. Author's note
- Great seaside location for cheap and simple camping.

2517600E 5998700N

Hema Atlas Map Ref 39 G2

721
Map 16 B4

Tasman Motor Camp

Adjacent SH60 (Coastal Hwy), Ruby Bay
Ph/Fax (03) 540 2542 tasmancamping@xtra.co.nz

Popular camp handy to fruit picking seasonal work opportunities.

2517100E 6000000N
Hema Atlas Map Ref 39 G2

722
Map 16 B4

Helme Holiday Park

201 Kina Peninsula Rd, Kina Beach: 13km S of Motueka
Ph/Fax (03) 526 6848 helme@ts.co.nz

2514800E 6004700N
Hema Atlas Map Ref 39 F2

723
Map 16 B4

Fernwood Holiday Park

519 High St Sth, Motueka
Ph/Fax (03) 528 7488

Author's note - Handy to the centre of Motueka,
and a good base for seasonal fruit picking opportunities.

2511600E 6008800N
Hema Atlas Map Ref 39 F2

724
Map 16 A4

Motueka Top 10 Holiday Park

10 Fearon St, Motueka: signposted E of Motueka's
Main St, at the N end of town
Ph 0800 66 8835 info@motuekatop10.co.nz

Author's note - A well-managed camp that is very spacious
and sheltered.

2511800E 6012000N
Hema Atlas Map Ref 39 E2

725
Map 16 A4

Roadside Rest Area

Adjacent SH60, Motueka: NW side of the
Motueka River Bridge

2510700E 6013700N
Hema Atlas Map Ref 39 E2

726
Map 16 A4

Roadside Rest Area

Little Kaiteriteri: E of Kaiteriteri

Author's note - A beautiful beach that is now sadly rather
overshadowed by expensive subdivisions.

2511900E 6018200N
Hema Atlas Map Ref 39 E2

727
Map 16 A4

Kaiteriteri Beach Holiday Park

Sandy Bay Rd, Kaiteriteri: off SH60 N of Motueka
Ph (03) 527 8010 kaiteritericamp@xtra.co.nz

Author's note - A big bustling camp right on one of the
prettiest beaches in NZ, and a great base from which to explore
the Abel Tasman Park.

2511400E 6019700N
Hema Atlas Map Ref 39 E2

728
Map 16 A4

Marahau Beach Camp & Cabins

Franklin St, Marahau: signposted from the main
road at Marahau

Another handy base from which to explore the Abel Tasman Park.

2511400E 6022100N
Hema Atlas Map Ref 39 D2

729

Map 16 A4

Roadside Rest Area

Abel Tasman National Park, Marahau: NE of SH60

2511200E 6023300N
Hema Atlas Map Ref 38 F10

730

Map 16 A4

Roadside Rest Area

Abel Tasman National Park, beachside reserve: NE of SH60

2510000E 6024600N
Hema Atlas Map Ref 38 F10

731

Map 16 A4

Roadside Rest Area

Hawkes Lookout, Takaka Hill, SH60

2502500E 6021100N
Hema Atlas Map Ref 38 F9

732

Map 16 A4

Roadside Rest Area

Takaka Hilltop Walkway, SH60

2498700E 6020300N
Hema Atlas Map Ref 38 F8

733

Map 16 A4

Cobb Valley, Kahurangi National Park

Kahurangi National Park
DoC Nelson Regional Visitor Centre Ph (03) 546 9339
nelsonvc@doc.govt.nz
Stream water only

2477800E 6009300N
Hema Atlas Map Ref 37 H6

734

Map 16 A4

Roadside Rest Area

Lindsay Bridge Reserve, Takaka River: SH60

2495400E 6025000N
Hema Atlas Map Ref 38 F8

735

14 E1 16 A4

Roadside Rest Area

Paynes Ford Scenic Reserve: SH60

2494500E 6035200N
Hema Atlas Map Ref 38 E8

736

14 E1 16 A4

Takaka Caravan & Motel Park

56 Motupipi St, Takaka: signposted on the Takaka
to Pohara Rd, from the S end of Takaka main street
Ph (03) 525 7300 www.holidayparks.co.nz/takakacaravan
Author's note - Handy to the centre of Takaka.

2494400E 6039400N
Hema Atlas Map Ref 38 E8

737

Map
14 E1 16 A4

Pohara Beach Top 10 Motor Camp

Abel Tasman Dr, Pohara: 11km from SH60 at Takaka
Ph 0800 764 272 pohara@xtra.co.nz

Author's note - Beachside and handy to some nice cafes, with
the town of Takaka down the road and the Abel Tasman National Park
at your back door.

2498700E 6042100N
Hema Atlas Map Ref 38 D8

738

14 E1 16 A4

Roadside Rest Area

Pohara Beach Reserve: 11km from SH60 at Takaka

2499900E 6042100N
Hema Atlas Map Ref 38 D8

739

14 E1 16 A4

Roadside Rest Area

Tarakohe Beach Reserve, Abel Tasman Dr:
off SH60 at Takaka

2502600E 6043100N
Hema Atlas Map Ref 38 D9

740

14 E1 16 A4

Roadside Rest Area

Tata Beach Reserve, Abel Tasman Dr: off SH60 at Takaka

2502500E 6044500N
Hema Atlas Map Ref 38 D9

741

Map 14 E2
16 A4

Totaranui, Abel Tasman National Park

Totaranui Beach, Abel Tasman National Park:
signposted about 32km from Takaka
DoC Nelson Regional Visitor Centre Ph (03) 546 9339
nelsonvc@doc.govt.nz Bookings Ph (03) 528 8083

Cold shower only Author's note - A nice beach base to explore the
Abel Tasman National Park. The road is not recommended for
caravans, trailers or big rigs.

2509700E 6043500N
Hema Atlas Map Ref 38 D10

742

14 E1 16 A4

Roadside Rest Area

SH60: just S of the Pupu Springs turnoff

2492000E 6041200N
Hema Atlas Map Ref 38 D8

743

14 E1 16 A4

Roadside Rest Area

Patons Rock Reserve: 2km N of SH60, NW of Takaka

2490300E 6046200N
Hema Atlas Map Ref 38 D8

744

Map 14 E1
16 A4

Golden Bay Holiday Park

Tukurua Beach: signposted N of SH60
Ph (03) 525 9742 goldenbay.holiday@xtra.co.nz

Author's note - With its own beach, this sheltered camp is one
of the best in the Bay.

2485400E 6052100N
Hema Atlas Map Ref 37 C7

745

Map 14 E1
16 A4

Collingwood Motor Camp

William St, Collingwood: at the W end
of Collingwood's main street

A caretaker may collect fees if they are in attendance. Author's note -
Simple camping in a small waterfont location that's handy to the town.

2484000E 6058900N
Hema Atlas Map Ref 37 C7

746

Pakawau Beach Park

Beachside at Pakawau on SH60: 13km N of Collingwood
Ph (03) 524 8327 stay@pakawau.co.nz

Author's note - Waterfront, small, neat and tidy spot that's a great base from which to explore Cape Farewell.

Map 14 E1
16 A4

2484200E 6067000N
Hema Atlas Map Ref 37 B7

747

Farewell Gardens Holiday Park

Adjacent SH60, Port Puponga: 22km N of Collingwood

A caretaker may collect fees if they are in attendance. Author's note - The closest camp to Cape Farewell and Farewell Spit Conservation Farm Park.

Map 14 E1
16 A4

2487900E 6075100N
Hema Atlas Map Ref 37 A7

748

Roadside Rest Area

Seddon St Reserve, Port Puponga: 22km N of Collingwood

Map 14 E1
16 A4

2489100E 6075100N
Hema Atlas Map Ref 37 A7

749

Roadside Rest Area

Wharariki Beach Reserve: N of Port Puponga

Map 14 E1
16 A4

2482600E 6077900N
Hema Atlas Map Ref 37 A7

SH6 - Richmond to Inangahua Junction (SH69)

750

Quinney's Bush Camp and Caravan Park

SH6, Motupiko: S of Richmond
Ph (03) 522 4249 quinneys-bush@xtra.co.nz

Author's note - A fabulous riverside camp, and ideal if you are travelling with children as there is quite a lot to entertain them.

Map 16 B4

2495100E 5971900N
Hema Atlas Map Ref 42 C13

751

Tapawera Settle

19 Tadmor Valley Rd, Tapawera: signposted from the Motueka Valley Hwy, at the N end of town
Ph (03) 522 4334

Author's note - Small but friendly.

Map 16 B4

2494500E 5980800N
Hema Atlas Map Ref 42 B13

752

Siberia Flat, Kahurangi National Park

Wangapeka Valley, Kahurangi National Park
DoC Nelson Regional Visitor Centre Ph (03) 546 9339
nelsonvc@doc.govt.nz

Stream water only

Map 16 B4

2475800E 5974400N
Hema Atlas Map Ref 42 C11

753

Roadside Rest Area

Mcleans Recreational Reserve, Motueka Valley Hwy: adjacent the Motueka River

Author's note - Riverside picnic and swimming spot with free camping options.

Map 16 B4

2493200E 5990400N
Hema Atlas Map Ref 42 A13

754 | **Kawatiri Junction, Kahurangi National Park** | $ 🚻 🛏 📷 🚶

Riverside at the intersection of SH63 & SH6
DoC Nelson Lakes Visitor Centre Ph (03) 521 1806
starnaudao@doc.govt.nz

2478700E 5946300N
Author's note - Nice short walks from this spot.
Hema Atlas Map Ref 42 F11

Map 16 B4

---

755 | **Roadside Rest Area**

SH6: SE of Gowanbridge

2472800E 5944700N
Hema Atlas Map Ref 42 F11

Map 16 B4

---

756 | **Roadside Rest Area** | 🚻

Gowan Bridge Reserve, SH6
St Arnaud DoC Visitor Information Centre -
Ph (03) 521 1806 starnaudao@doc.govt.nz

2473800E 5943300N
Hema Atlas Map Ref 42 F11

Map 16 B4

---

757 | **Gowan River Holiday Camp** | $ 🚻 🚰 🚿 🛖 📷 🛏 🚶 ⛽

Gowan Valley Road: S of SH6 afrom Gowanbridge
Ph (03) 523 9921

2476200E 5939300N
Open Labour weekend through summer
Hema Atlas Map Ref 42 G11

Map 16 B4

---

758 | **Lake Rotoroa, Nelson Lakes National Park** | ✓ $ 🚻 🚰 📷 🚶

Lake Rotoroa: signposted E of SH6 about \5km S
of the Kawatiri intersection
DoC Nelson Lakes Visitor Centre Ph (03) 521 1806
starnaudao@doc.govt.nz

2476300E 5935600N
Author's note - Magic spot with good walks and fishing.
Hema Atlas Map Ref 42 G11

Map 16 B4

---

759 | **Roadside Rest Area**

SH6: W of Gowanbridge

2468000E 5944700N
Hema Atlas Map Ref 42 F10

Map 16 B3

---

760 | **Owen River Recreation Reserve** | $ 🚻 🛏 🚿 📷 🚶

Beside the Owen River Hotel on SH6: 20km N of Murchison
Casual Camping - a caretaker may collect fees - if they are
in attendance. Enquiries to the Owen River Hotel.

2464200E 5947500N
Hema Atlas Map Ref 42 F10

Map 16 B3

---

761 | **Roadside Rest Area**

SH6: S of Owen River

2460500E 5940000N
Hema Atlas Map Ref 42 F10

Map 16 B3

---

762 | **Roadside Rest Area**

Mangles River Bridge, SH6: N of Murchison

2456900E 5935900N
Hema Atlas Map Ref 42 G9

Map 16 B3

763
Map 16 B3

Riverview Holiday Park
Riverview Tce, Murchison: N end of Murchison
township, signposted from SH6
Ph (03) 523 9591 riverviewhp@xtra.co.nz
Author's note - Great riverside base for rafting and
canoeing in a parklike setting.

2455200E 5934900N
Hema Atlas Map Ref 42 G9

764
Map 16 B3

Kiwi Park Holiday Park
170 Fairfax St, Murchison: signposted S of Murchison,
signposted from Murchison town centre
Ph 0800 22 80 80 kiwipark@xtra.co.nz
Author's note - Modern facilities in a compact rural location.

2454500E 5933000N
Hema Atlas Map Ref 42 G9

765
Map 16 C3

Roadside Rest Area
Maruia Falls, SH65: near Ariki, approx 6km
S of the intersection with SH6

Author's note - Nice waterfall views.

2447200E 5927500N
Hema Atlas Map Ref 42 H8

766
Map 16 B3

Lyell
SH6, Upper Buller Gorge: 10km NE of Inangahua
www.doc.govt.nz or Reefton Visitor Centre
Ph (03) 732 8391 reeftoninfo@paradise.net.nz

2428100E 5933500N
Hema Atlas Map Ref 41 G6

SH1 & SH63 - Picton to St Arnaud via Blenheim

767
Map 17 B5

Rarangi
Port Underwood Rd, Rarangi
www.doc.govt.nz or Picton Visitor Information Centre
Ph (03) 520 3113 pivc@destinationmarlborough.com

2598200E 5981200N
Hema Atlas Map Ref 44 A11

768
Map 17 B5

Whites Bay
Port Underwood Rd, Rarangi: at Pukatea Stream
www.doc.govt.nz or Picton Visitor Information Centre
Ph (03) 520 3113 pivc@destinationmarlborough.com
Author's note - A beautiful secluded seaside spot with simple camping:
the gates close at night. It's a very pleasant place to use as a base
to explore Blenheim, or await the ferry.

2599000E 5979700N
Hema Atlas Map Ref 44 A11

769
Map 17 B5

Spring Creek Holiday Park
Rapaura Rd: near intersection with SH1
Ph (03) 570 5893

Author's note - Close to the many vineyards along Rapaura Rd.

2589500E 5972300N
Hema Atlas Map Ref 44 B10

770
Map 17 B5

Blenheim Bridge Top 10 Holiday Park
78 Grove Rd (SH1), Blenheim: just N of Blenheim
Ph 0800 26 86 66 blenheimtop10@xtra.co.nz
Author's note - A four-star-rated Top 10 park that's handy to the centre
of Blenheim and not far from the ferries.

2591000E 5966700N
Hema Atlas Map Ref 44 C11

771

Map 17 B5

Duncannon Holiday Park

SH1, Blenheim: 2km S of Blenheim's centre
Ph 0800 697 895 duncannon@xtra.co.nz
Author's note - Sheltered spot that's a useful base for the
Cook Strait ferry and viticulture delights of the area.

2592200E 5965800N
Hema Atlas Map Ref 44 C11

772

Map 17 B5

Onamalutu

Onamalutu Rd (nth bank of Wairau Flats):
take Northbank Rd off SH6, N of Renwick
www.doc.govt.nz or Picton Visitor Information Centre
Ph (03) 520 3113 pivc@destinationmarlborough.com

2572700E 5969500N
Hema Atlas Map Ref 44 C9

773

Map 17 B5

Mill Flat

Pine Valley: 22km up Northbank Rd, NW
of Blenheim (4WD only)
www.doc.govt.nz or Picton Visitor Information Centre
Ph (03) 520 3113 pivc@destinationmarlborough.com
Stream water only

2553800E 5964200N
Hema Atlas Map Ref 43 C4

774

Map 17 B5

Wairau Valley Holiday Park

SH63, Wairau Valley
Wairau Valley Tavern Ph (03) 572 2878
Author's note - Little more than a hot and dusty paddock
adjoining the local pub.

2554300E 5961100N
Hema Atlas Map Ref 43 D7

775

Map 16 B4

Kowhai Point

Adjacent SH63, Wash Bridge, Wairau River
DoC Nelson Lakes Visitor Centre Ph (03) 521 1806
starnaudao@doc.govt.nz
Stream water only

2518200E 5944100N
Hema Atlas Map Ref 43 E3

776

Map 16 C4

Cold Water Stream

Hanmer Rd, Rainbow Valley: turn S off SH63
about 11km E of St Arnaud
DoC Nelson Lakes Visitor Centre Ph (03) 521 1806
starnaudao@doc.govt.nz
Open Dec to March

2504200E 5905600N
Hema Atlas Map Ref 43 J2

777

Map 16 B4

Kerr Bay, Nelson Lakes National Park

Eastern Bay of Lake Rotoiti, St Arnaud: off SH63
DoC Nelson Lakes Visitor Centre Ph (03) 521 1806
starnaudao@doc.govt.nz

2496800E 5933000N
Hema Atlas Map Ref 42 G13

778

Map 16 B4

West Bay, Nelson Lakes National Park

Signposted 2km W of St Arnaud: off SH63
DoC Nelson Lakes Visitor Centre Ph (03) 521 1806
starnaudao@doc.govt.nz

2495500E 5933900N
Hema Atlas Map Ref 42 G13

779

Roadside Rest Area

Glenhope Reserve, SH63: S of junction with SH6

Map 16 B4

2478700E 5944700N

Hema Atlas Map Ref 42 F12

WEST COAST REGION

Lake Matheson

SH6 - Inangahua Junction (SH69) to Greymouth

780

Roadside Rest Area

Kilkenny Lookout: adjacent SH6 and the Buller River

Map 16 C3

2408300E 5927200N

Hema Atlas Map Ref 41 H4

781

Roadside Rest Area

SH6: E of Wesptort

Map 16 C3

2400100E 5929900N

Hema Atlas Map Ref 41 G4

782

Little Beach Café, Motel & Camping

Adjacent SH6, Little Beach: signposted on N side
of Little Totara Stream

A caretaker may collect fees if they are in attendance.
Author's note - Simple camping in a pretty and peaceful setting.

Map 16 C2

2383800E 5924700N

Hema Atlas Map Ref 41 H2

783

Charleston Motor Camp

4 Darkies Terrace Rd, Charleston: signposted
next to Charleston Hotel
Ph (03) 789 6773 cmcamp@xtra.co.nz

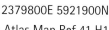 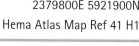

Map 16 C2

2379800E 5921900N

Hema Atlas Map Ref 41 H1

784

Roadside Rest Area

Irimahuwheri scenic viewpoint, SH6: S of Charleston

Author's note - Magic coastal views: on a clear day you can even see
Mt Cook to the south.

Map 16 C2

2373300E 5902300N

Hema Atlas Map Ref 45 A5

785

Roadside Rest Area

Pororari River Walkway, SH6: N of Punakaiki

Map 16 C2

2373500E 5898700N

Hema Atlas Map Ref 45 B5

786
Map 16 C2

Punakaiki Beach Camp

Owen St, Punakaiki: off SH6, at N end of Punakaiki township
Ph (03) 731 1894 beachcamp@xtra.co.nz

Author's note - With the pounding sea at your doorstep this site
is a great base to explore the walks and Punakaiki rocks.

2371700E 5899000N
Hema Atlas Map Ref 45 B5

787
Map 16 C2

Roadside Rest Area

W of SH6: S of Punakaiki, at Thirteen Mile Creek

2367700E 5876400N
Hema Atlas Map Ref 45 D4

788
Map 16 C2

Roadside Rest Area

Adjacent SH6: S of Punakaiki

2366200E 5873900N
Hema Atlas Map Ref 45 D4

789
Map 16 C2

Roadside Rest Area

Strongman Mine Memorial, W of SH6: N of Rapahoe

2365500E 5871900N
Hema Atlas Map Ref 45 D4

790
Map 16 C2

Rapahoe Beach Motor Camp

10 Hawken St, Rapahoe: signposted W of SH6 at Rapahoe
Ph/Fax (03) 762 7025 rapahoebeach@xtra.co.nz

Author's note - Beachside spot that is 'budget' but charming.

2364600E 5869400N
Hema Atlas Map Ref 45 E4

SH67 - Westport to Karamea

791
Map 16 B2

Roadside Rest Area

SH67: on the N side of the Buller River Bridge at the
S entrance to Westport

2393800E 5937600N
Hema Atlas Map Ref 41 G3

792
Map 16 B2

Westport Holiday Park & Motel

31-37 Domett St, Westport: signposted from
the main street
Ph (03) 789 7043 westportholidaypark@xtra.co.nz

Author's note - Sheltered camping spot in parklike grounds that's
handy to the centre of Westport.

2393800E 5939000N
Hema Atlas Map Ref 41 G3

793
Map 16 B2

The Happy Wanderer

56 Russell St, Westport
Ph (03) 789 8627

Purpose-built hostel with tent and campervan sites.

2393800E 5939000N
Hema Atlas Map Ref 41 G3

794   **Seal Colony Top 10 Holiday Park**

Marine Parade, Carters Beach: signposted on SH67A
to Cape Foulwind

Map 16 B2

Author's note - Beachside spot in a pretty location that's handy
to parks, playgrounds and a nice café.

2389400E 5939200N
Hema Atlas Map Ref 41 G2

---

795   **Railway Tavern & Accommodation**

4 Newcastle St, Waimangaroa
Ph (03) 789 9863

Map 16 B3

Author's note - Traditional West Coast camping.

2406400E 5944100N
Hema Atlas Map Ref 41 F4

---

796   **The Big Fish Hotel**

117 Torea St, Granity
Ph (03) 782 8011

Map 16 B3

Author's note - Beachside traditional West Coast camping.

2413100E 5951500N
Hema Atlas Map Ref 41 E5

---

797   **Seddonville Holiday Park**

108 Gladstone St, Seddonville: 4km inland from SH67
Ph (03) 782 1314

Map 16 B3

Author's note - Simple camping in an old school.

2425400E 5960500N
Hema Atlas Map Ref 41 D6

---

798   **Gentle Annie Point Camp & Café**

A 2km diversion from SH67

A caretaker may collect fees if they are in attendance.
Author's note - A beautiful base from which to explore
Map 16 B3   Seddonville, surf or fish.

2422600E 5966100N
Hema Atlas Map Ref 41 D6

---

799   **Little Wanganui Hotel & Camping Ground**

SH67, Little Wanganui
Ph (03) 782 6752

Map 16 B3

Tent sites only. Author's note - Traditional West Coast camping.

2433100E 5981600N
Hema Atlas Map Ref 41 B7

---

800   **Courthouse Flat, Kahurangi National Park**

Wangapeka Valley, Kahurangi National Park: adjoins
historic goldfield
DoC Nelson Regional Visitor Centre Ph (03) 546 9339
nelsonvc@doc.govt.nz

Map 16 B3

Stream water only

2441800E 5984700N
Hema Atlas Map Ref 42 B8

---

801   **Karamea Holiday Park**

67 Maori Point Rd, Karamea: 2km S of Karamea township
Ph (03) 782 6758 info@karamea.com

Map 16 B3

Author's note - Nice sheltered camping on an estuary south of Karamea.

2434600E 5993700N
Hema Atlas Map Ref 41 A7

802

Map 16 B3

Karamea Domain Camping Ground

Waverly St, Karamea: signposted W of Karamea town centre

A caretaker may collect fees if they are in attendance.
Author's note - Simple camping handy to the centre of Karamea.

2434700E 5995200N
Hema Atlas Map Ref 41 A7

803

Map 16 B3

Oparara Basin, Kahurangi National Park

Kahurangi National Park: 45 minute drive NE of Karamea
www.doc.govt.nz or Karamea Information & Resource
Centre Ph (03) 7826 652 info@karameainfo.co.nz

Author's note - World-class scenic treats await those daring to
explore this beautiful valley but there is no camping in this vicinity,
and the access road is not suited to big rigs and caravans.

2442100E 6008300N
Hema Atlas Map Ref 37 H3

804

Map 16 B3

Kohaihai, Kahurangi National Park

Kohaihai River mouth, Kahurangi National Park:
15km N of Karamea
www.doc.govt.nz or Karamea Information & Resource
Centre Ph (03) 7826 652 info@karameainfo.co.nz

Author's note - Simple, picturesque camping at the start/end
of the Heaphy Track. Insect repellent is essential.

2434000E 6009900N
Hema Atlas Map Ref 37 H2

SH7 - Reefton to Greymouth

805

Map 16 C3

Reefton Domain Motor Camp

Ross St, Reefton: signposted off SH7 at E side
of Reefton township
Ph (03) 732 8477

A caretaker may collect fees if they are in attendance. Author's note
- Simple camping that's handy to Reefton's town centre.

2416700E 5898800N
Hema Atlas Map Ref 46 B9

806

Map 16 C3

Roadside Rest Area

Tawhai Reserve, SH7: S of Reefton

2411500E 5895800N
Hema Atlas Map Ref 46 B9

807

Map 16 C3

Slab Creek

Slab Creek Rd, off SH7: a 2km diversion from SH7
approx 10km S of Reefton
www.doc.govt.na or Westport Visitor Centre
Ph (03) 789 6658 westport.info@xtra.co.nz

Author's note - Nice streamside location with tame wekas.

2410900E 5893700N
Hema Atlas Map Ref 46 B9

808

Map 16 C3

Ikamatua Holiday Park

218 Main Rd, Ikamatua: beside the Ikamatua Hotel
Ikamatua Hotel Ph (03) 732 3555

Author's note - Traditional West Coast camping.

2401000E 5881700N
Hema Atlas Map Ref 46 C8

809 Nelson Creek Reserve

Map 16 C2

Nelson Creek: 5km E of SH7

A caretaker may collect fees or make a donation to the local hotel. Author's note - Charming wee township with nice walks and a pleasant stream adjoining the campsite.

2388800E 5866300N

Hema Atlas Map Ref 45 E6

---

810 The Old Steam Engine Roadside Rest Area

E of SH7: NE of Stillwater

Map 16 C2

2379800E 5865000N

Hema Atlas Map Ref 45 E5

---

811 Lake Brunner Country Motel

Map 16 D2

2014 Arnold Valley Rd: about 1km NW of Moana
Ph 0508 738 014 lbcmotel@xtra.co.nz

Author's note - Modern facilities in a parklike setting adjoining a native bush reserve.

2385900E 5848900N

Hema Atlas Map Ref 45 G6

---

812 Lake Brunner Motor Camp

Map 16 D2

Ahau St, Moana: signposted from the centre of Moana
Ph/Fax (03) 738 0600

Author's note - Handy to the lake, boat ramp and town centre, but there is little shelter.

2384500E 5847000N

Hema Atlas Map Ref 45 G6

SH6 - Greymouth to Franz Josef

813 Central Motor Home Park

Map 16 C2

117 Tainui St, Greymouth: At rear of Caltex Station, just S of town centre

A caretaker may collect fees if they are in attendance. Author's note - There's tarseal camping for campervans, and it's handy to the town centre.

2361700E 5860300N

Hema Atlas Map Ref 118 B4, 45 E4

---

814 Greymouth Seaside Top 10 Holiday Park

Map 16 C2

2 Chesterfield St, Greymouth: signposted W of SH6, S of town centre
Ph 0800 867 104 info@top10greymouth.co.nz

Author's note - Well appointed, as you expect from Top 10, and next to the beach.

2360200E 5858500N

Hema Atlas Map Ref 45 F4

---

815 South Beach Motor Park

Map 16 C2

318 Main South Rd, South Beach: W of SH6, 8km S of Greymouth
Ph 0800 101 222 stay@southbeach.co.nz

2359600E 5856400N

Hema Atlas Map Ref 45 F3

---

816 KJ's Accommodation & Camping

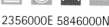

Map 16 D2

SH6: 50m W of Kumara Junction
Ph (03) 736 9558

Author's note - Funky camping in the grounds of the old Kumara School.

2356000E 5846000N

Hema Atlas Map Ref 45 G3

817

Map 16 D2

Goldsborough

Stafford Dillmanstown Rd, Goldsborough Valley:
17km from Hokitika

2356500E 5835800N
Hema Atlas Map Ref 45 H3

818

Map 16 D2

Jaquie Grant's Place

Greyhound Rd: W of SH6, 6km N of Hokitika

A caretaker may collect fees if they are in attendance. Author's note
- This site has near new facilities, and it's handy to Hokitika.

2346600E 5835800N
Hema Atlas Map Ref 45 H2

819

Map 16 D2

Shining Star Beachfront Accommodation

11 Richards Dr, Hokitika: W of SH6, 1km N of
Hokitika town centre
Ph 0800 744 646 shining@xtra.co.nz

Author's note - This site has nice facilities and it's opposite
glowworm caves for nightime entertainment.

2343100E 5831300N
Hema Atlas Map Ref 45 H2

820

Map 16 D2

252 Beachside Holiday Park

252 Revell St, Hokitika: signposted W of the town centre
Ph 0508 252 252 info@252beachside.co.nz

Author's note - Although this site is handy to the beach
it is more suited to mobile homes.

2343100E 5831300N
Hema Atlas Map Ref 45 H2

821

Map 16 D2

Hokitika Holiday Park

242 Stafford St, Hokitika: signposted E of the
town centre, near the dairy factory
Ph 0800 465 436 holidaypark@hokitika.com

Author's note - This three-star-rated older style camp, in sheltered
and spacious grounds, is in a quiet location.

2344600E 5830300N
Hema Atlas Map Ref 45 H2

822

Map 16 D2

Hans Bay-Lake Kaniere

Lake Kaniere Rd: 19km E of Hokitika

2359700E 5820800N
Hema Atlas Map Ref 45 J3

823

Map 16 D2

Lake Mahinapua

E of SH6: 16km S of Hokitika
DoC Arthur's Pass Visitor Centre Ph (03) 318 9211
arthurspassvc@doc.govt.nz

Author's note - A simple, scenic, lakeside camping spot that's
close to Hokitika.

2338900E 5821900N
Hema Atlas Map Ref 45 J1

824

Map 16 D2

Ross Historic Goldfields Reserve

SH6: NE end of main street in Ross, 28km S of Hokitika

Interesting walks, goldpanning, and some lovely old buildings.

2332900E 5810000N
Hema Atlas Map Ref 50 B11

825   **Roadside Rest Area**

Fergusons Bush Scenic Reserve, adjacent SH6:
approx 10km S of Ross

Map 16 D2

2326500E 5807700N
Hema Atlas Map Ref 50 B10

---

826   **Pukekura Lodge (The Bushman's Centre)**

Adjacent SH6, Pukekura: 22km S of Ross
Ph (03) 755 4144 pete&tjustine@pukekura.co.nz

Author's note - Funky camping with rustic West Coast hospitality;
adjoining the 'road kill café' and bar.

Map 16 D2

2320800E 5796600N
Hema Atlas Map Ref 50 C10

---

827   **Ianthe**

Lake Ianthe, adjacent SH6: 15km N Harihari
DoC Franz Josef Visitor Information Centre
Ph (03) 752 0796 franzjosefvc@doc.govt.nz

Map 16 D1

Author's note - This is a beautiful spot but insect repellent is a must.

2316600E 5792200N
Hema Atlas Map Ref 50 C9

---

828   **Harihari Motor Inn**

Adjacent SH6, Harihari
Ph (03) 753 3026

Map 16 D1

Author's note - Beachside, traditional West Coast camping.

2312000E 5782100N
Hema Atlas Map Ref 50 D9

---

829   **Roadside Rest Area**

E side of SH6, S end of Harihari

Map 16 D1

2311200E 5780600N
Hema Atlas Map Ref 50 D9

---

830   **Roadside Rest Area**

Whataroa Scenic Reserve, adjacent SH6

16 E1 19 A5

2299000E 5766700N
Hema Atlas Map Ref 49 F7

---

831   **Okarito Camping Ground**

Russell St, Okarito: a 14km diversion W of SH6

A caretaker may collect fees if they are in attendance. Author's note
- Simple camping in a very pretty part of the world.

16 E1 19 A5

2279000E 5772900N
Hema Atlas Map Ref 49 E5

---

832   **Okarito Car Park**

Okarito: 14km W of SH6

16 E1 19 A5

2278600E 5771700N
Hema Atlas Map Ref 49 E5

---

833   **Otto/MacDonalds**

Adjacent SH6: 15km N of Franz Josef
DoC Franz Josef Visitor Information Centre
Ph (03) 752 0796 franzjosefvc@doc.govt.nz

Map 16 E1
19 A5

Author's note - A peaceful and simple camping option less than
18km from the often crowded Franz Josef township.

2285800E 5764400N
Hema Atlas Map Ref 49 F6

834

Map 16 E1
19 A5

Roadside Rest Area

Lake Mapourika Reserve, SH6: 10km N of Franz Josef
DoC Franz Josef Visitor Information Centre
Ph (03) 752 0796 franzjosefvc@doc.govt.nz

2283300E 5760800N

Hema Atlas Map Ref 49 F6

SH6 - Franz Josef to Haast

835

Map 16 E1
19 A5

Franz Josef Mountain View Top 10 Holiday Park

2902 Franz Josef Hwy (SH6), Franz Josef Glacier:
1km N of the main township
Ph 0800 467 897 bookings@mountain-view.co.nz
Author's note - It pays to arrive early or book ahead, as accommodation
can be scarce in this area.

2280700E 5755700N

Hema Atlas Map Ref 49 G6

836

Map 16 E1
19 A5

Rainforest Retreat

46 Cron St, Franz Josef Glacier: one block E of SH6
in the centre of Franz Josef
Ph (03) 752 0220 comestay@forestretreat.co.nz
Author's note - It pays to arrive early or book ahead, as accommodation
can be scarce in this area.

2282400E 5754500N

Hema Atlas Map Ref 49 G6

837

Map 16 E1
19 A5

Fox Glacier Lodge

Sullivan Rd, Fox Glacier: signposted at the S end
of Fox Glacier, E of SH6
Ph/Fax (03) 751 0888 foxglacierlodge@xtra.co.nz
Author's note - This lodge is in a handy, central location but it is only
really suited to caravans and campervans.

2269400E 5744300N

Hema Atlas Map Ref 49 H4

838

Map 16 E1
19 A5

Fox Glacier Viewpoint

E of SH6, Fox Glacier

Author's note - There are scenic views of the glacier, and walks
east of this point.

2271400E 5742000N

Hema Atlas Map Ref 49 H5

839

Map 16 E1
19 A5

Fox Glacier Holiday Park

Forks Rd, Fox Glacier: signposted W of Fox Glacier & SH6
on the Lake Matheson Rd, 800m from the town centre
Ph 0800 154 366 info@foxglacierholidaypark.co.nz
Author's note - It pays to arrive early or book ahead, as accommodation
can be scarce in this area.

2267800E 5745900N

Hema Atlas Map Ref 49 H4

840

Map 16 E1
18 A4

Lake Matheson Roadside Rest Area

Lake Matheson: 3km W of Fox Glacier town centre
DoC Fox Glacier Visitor Information Centre
Ph (03) 751 0807 foxglaciervc@doc.govt.nz
Author's note - This stop is a must for the famous mirror-lake
views from Lake Matheson - it is stunning if the mountains are
clear and there is no wind (a rare combination).

2264000E 5746500N

Hema Atlas Map Ref 49 H4

841

Peak Lookout Roadside Rest Area

After the Lake Matheson turnoff on the Gillespies Beach Rd:
W of SH6

Map 16 E1
18 A4

2260900E 5746500N

Hema Atlas Map Ref 49 H4

842

Gillespies Beach

N end of Gillespies Beach: 22km from Fox Glacier,
a half hour drive along a twisting gravel drive west
from the Lake Matheson turnoff
DoC Fox Glacier Visitor Information Centre
Ph (03) 751 0807 foxglaciervc@doc.govt.nz

Map 16 E1
18 A4

Author's note – This is an interesting part of the world, with
a seal colony nearby and nice views of the Alps.

2253200E 5750300N

Hema Atlas Map Ref 49 G3

843

Roadside Rest Area

Westland National Park, SH6: the Copland Track
starts from this point

Map 16 E1
18 A4

2251900E 5733000N

Hema Atlas Map Ref 49 J3

844

Roadside Rest Area

Bruce Bay Reserve, SH6

Map 18 A4

2235400E 5729700N

Hema Atlas Map Ref 58 A13

845

South Westland Salmon Farm & Café Roadside Rest Area

SH6

Map 18 A4

2228400E 5715300N

Hema Atlas Map Ref 58 B12

846

Lake Paringa

W of SH6, Lake Paringa, beside Jamie Ck: 40km N of Haast
DoC Haast Visitor Centre Ph (03) 750 0809
haastvc@doc.govt.nz

Map 18 A4

Stream water only Author's note – This is a pretty spot but insect
repellent is essential.

2220500E 5715000N

Hema Atlas Map Ref 58 B12

847

Roadside Rest Area

SH6: near the Haast-Paringa Track
DoC Haast Visitor Centre Ph (03) 750 0809
haastvc@doc.govt.nz

Map 18 A4

2216400E 5709300N

Hema Atlas Map Ref 58 C11

848

Munro Beach Track Roadside Rest Area

SH6, near Lake Moeraki

Map 18 A4

2210000E 5715100N

Hema Atlas Map Ref 58 B11

849 Roadside Rest Area

Knights Point Lookout, SH6: N of Haast

Map 18 A4

2205600E 5715300N
Hema Atlas Map Ref 58 B10

---

850 Roadside Rest Area

Ships Creek Reserve, SH6: N of Haast
DoC Haast Visitor Centre Ph (03) 750 0809
haastvc@doc.govt.nz

Map 18 A4

Author's note - There are interesting forest and coastal walk options
from this point, but insect repellent is essential.

2199500E 5710000N
Hema Atlas Map Ref 58 B9

---

851 Roadside Rest Area

N shore of the Haast River Bridge

Map 18 A3

2192400E 5699100N
Hema Atlas Map Ref 58 D9

---

852 Haast Lodge

Marks Rd, Haast: E of Haast township
Ph (03) 750 0703 haast_lodge@xtra.co.nz

Map 18 B3

Author's note - This former warehouse, now providing backpacker
accommodation, a caravan park and some camping, is functional
but not pretty.

2191700E 5694300N
Hema Atlas Map Ref 58 D9

---

853 Haast Beach Holiday Park

Jackson Bay Rd: 18km S of Haast River
Ph (03) 750 0860 haastpark@xtra.co.nz

Map 18 B3

Author's note - This simple and functional park is very popular during
the whitebaiting season.

2180400E 5692400N
Hema Atlas Map Ref 58 D8

Franz Josef Glacier. Photo Michelle Bignell

CANTERBURY REGION

Arthur's Pass. Photo: Donna Blaber

SH1 - Blenheim to Waipara (SH7)

854
Map 17 B5

Awatere-Seddon Domain Motor Camp
Seddon Domain, Foster St, Seddon: turn off SH1
S of Seddon township

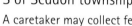

A caretaker may collect fees if they are in attendance. Author's note - Although it is handy to Seddon's swimming pool, the camp is rather exposed to summer heat and has little shade.

2600200E 5948200N
Hema Atlas Map Ref 44 E12

855
Map 17 B5

Awatere Rest Area
Adjacent SH1, S of Seddon

2601500E 5946000N
Hema Atlas Map Ref 44 E12

856
Map 17 B5

Marfells Beach
Marfells Beach, Lake Grassmere: off SH1
www.doc.govt.nz or Picton Visitor Information Centre
Ph (03) 546 9339 nelsonvc@doc.govt.na
Boil all water before drinking

2610800E 5942300N
Hema Atlas Map Ref 44 E13

857
Map 17 C5

Mororimu Rest Area
Adjacent SH1, N of Kaikoura

2581000E 5889500N
Hema Atlas Map Ref 48 C14

858
Map 17 C5

Waipapa Bay Camping Ground
Adjacent SH1, N of Kaikoura
Ph (03) 319 6340 waipapa.bay@xtra.co.nz

Author's note - Simple camping with the opportunity to purchase or catch crayfish.

2582800E 5887900N
Hema Atlas Map Ref 48 C14

859
Map 17 C5

Roadside Rest Area
Adjacent SH1, about 23km N of Kaikoura

Author's note - You can purchase yummy cooked crayfish at this spot.

2577500E 5882800N
Hema Atlas Map Ref 48 C13

860

Map 17 C5

Roadside Rest Area

Adjacent SH1, about 20km N of Kaikoura

2575200E 5880400N

Hema Atlas Map Ref 48 C13

861

Map 17 C5

A1 Kaikoura Motels & Holiday Park

9-15 Beach Rd, Kaikoura
Ph (03) 319 5999 kaikouramotel@xtra.co.nz

Author's note - The closest campsite to the centre of Kaikoura, this park has good facilities.

2566600E 5867900N

Hema Atlas Map Ref 48 E12

862

Map 17 C5

Kaikoura Top 10 Holiday Park

34 Beach Rd, Kaikoura: N of Kaikoura town centre
Ph 0800 36 36 38 kaikouratop10@xtra.co.nz

Author's note - This is four-star camping, and it even has a spa. The only negative is its close proximity to rail traffic.

2566600E 5867900N

Hema Atlas Map Ref 48 E12

863

Map 17 C5

69 Beach Rd Holiday Park

69 Beach Rd, Kaikoura: N of Kaikoura town centre
Ph/Fax (03) 319 6275 or 0800 692 322
69holidaypark@actrix.gen.nz

2566600E 5867900N

Hema Atlas Map Ref 48 E12

864

Map 17 C5

Peketa Beach Holiday Park

Adjacent SH1, 9km S of Kaikoura
Ph (03) 319 6299 kaikoura@peketabeach.co.nz

Author's note - This park is right next to the beach for swimming and fishing.

2559300E 5863500N

Hema Atlas Map Ref 48 E11

865

Map 17 C5

Goose Bay Camping

Adjacent SH1, 17km S of Kaikoura

A caretaker may collect fees if they are in attendance. Several coastal options are offered from this base stretching from Paia Point in the north to Omihi Bay and Boat Harbour in the south.

2552600E 5859200N

Hema Atlas Map Ref 48 F11

866

Map 16 D4

The Staging Post

Hawkswood: off SH1
Ph (03) 319 2824 or (03) 319 2715 www.kaikouratrack.co.nz
sally@kaikouratrack.co.nz

Author's note - This is a pleasant farmstay environment, and a base for the Kaikoura Coast walking track.

2537500E 5839900N

Hema Atlas Map Ref 48 H9

867

Map 16 D4

Cheviot Motels & Caravan Park

Levin Rd, Cheviot: W of town centre
Ph (03) 319 8607

Author's note - New owners are revitalising this camp.

2531400E 5822700N

Hema Atlas Map Ref 48 J9

868 Gore Bay & Buxton Campgrounds

Map 16 D4

Gore Bay: 8km SE of Cheviot

A caretaker may collect fees if they are in attendance. Author's note - There are numerous camping options in a relatively sheltered bay adjoining a favoured surfing and swimming beach.

2536100E 5817100N

Hema Atlas Map Ref 54 A13

869 Greta Valley Rest Area

Map 16 D4

SH1: 100m E

2508000E 5805600N

Hema Atlas Map Ref 54 B10

870 Greta Valley Camping Ground

Map 16 D4

SH1: 800m E
Ph 025 290 7061

A caretaker may collect fees if they are in attendance. Author's note - This spot is in a nice sheltered valley with the basics provided.

2507700E 5804000N

Hema Atlas Map Ref 54 B10

SH7 - Waipara (SH1) to Reefton

871 Waipara Sleepers Motor Camp

Map 16 D4

200m from junction of SH1 & SH7, Waipara
Ph/Fax 03 314 6003

Author's note - This camp is a bit funky, with the opportunity to bunk down in old railway wagons and free eggs supplied if the hens feel generous.

2489600E 5795000N

Hema Atlas Map Ref 54 C8

872 Lake Taylor

Map 16 D3

Lake Sumner Rd: 74km NW of Amberley
DoC North Canterbury and Regional Visitor Information
Ph (03) 371 3706 northcantyvc@doc.govt.nz
Stream water only

2448300E 5824500N

Hema Atlas Map Ref 46 J12

873 Loch Katrine

Map 16 D3

Lake Sumner Rd: 81km NW of Amberley
(7km of 4WD-only track)
DoC North Canterbury and Regional Visitor Information
Ph (03) 371 3706 northcantyvc@doc.govt.nz
Stream water only

2445500E 5831600N

Hema Atlas Map Ref 46 H12

874 Watters Cottage Rest Area

Map 16 D4

Adjacent SH70 (Inland Rd): N of junction with SH7

Author's note - An opportunity to picnic in the grounds of an historic cobb cottage.

2504400E 5834700N

Hema Atlas Map Ref 47 H6

875 Waiau Motor Camp

Map 16 D4

Highfield St, Waiau: signposted from SH70 (Inland Rd), W end of town
Ph (03) 315 6672

Author's note - This camp has all the basics, but it is a bit exposed for my liking.

2512800E 5839900N

Hema Atlas Map Ref 47 H7

876 Roadside Rest Area

Adjacent SH70 (Inland Rd): N of Waiau

Map 16 D4

2518900E 5846800N
Hema Atlas Map Ref 47 G7

877 Mt Lyford Lodge

Mt Lyford Skifield, SH70 (Inland Rd): 23km N of Waiau,
60km S of Kaikoura
Ph (03) 315 6446 www.mtlyfordlodge.co.nz
Author's note - This lodge is a base for skiing in winter and
horse trekking.

Map 16 C4

2522400E 5856300N
Hema Atlas Map Ref 48 F8

878 Hanmer River Rest Areas

Either side of SH7A alongside Hanmer River: just N of SH7

Author's note - This is a nice riverside spot with some shelter from the
wind and sun.

Map 16 D4

2491800E 5848100N
Hema Atlas Map Ref 47 G5

879 Alpine Holiday Park

Jollies Pass Rd, Hanmer Springs: 2km N of the SH7 & SH7A
junction, 8km S of Hanmer Springs
Ph (03) 315 7478 alpineholidayapartments@xtra.co.nz

Map 16 D4

2493400E 5848200N
Hema Atlas Map Ref 47 G5

880 Mountain View Top 10 Holiday Park

Main Rd, Hanmer Springs
Ph 0800 90 45 45 mtview.hanmer@clear.net.nz
Author's note Although this park is the closest to the thermal pools,
it can get a bit crowded.

Map 16 C4

2496600E 5853500N
Hema Atlas Map Ref 47 F5

881 The Pines Holiday Park

158 Argelins Rd, Hanmer Springs
Ph (03) 315 7152 pinesholidaypark@xtra.co.nz

Map 16 C4

2495800E 5854800N
Hema Atlas Map Ref 47 F5

882 Alpine Adventure Holiday Park

200 Jacks Pass Rd, Hanmer Springs: signposted from
Hanmer Springs' main street
Ph (03) 315 7112 aatouristpark@xtra.co.nz
Author's note - Although this park isn't as close to the town centre as
the others it is set in 20 acres of park, spacious, sheltered and quiet,
with all the facilities you need.

Map 16 C4

2494500E 5855900N
Hema Atlas Map Ref 47 F5

883 Horsehoe Creek Rest Area

Adjacent SH7, Lewis Pass

Map 16 D4

2471100E 5846300N
Hema Atlas Map Ref 47 G3

884 Hope River Rest Area
Adjacent SH7, Lewis Pass

Map 16 D3

2465000E 5847100N
Hema Atlas Map Ref 47 G2

885 Lake Sumner Forest Park Rest Area
800m from SH7, Lewis Pass

Map 16 D3

2459800E 5847600N
Hema Atlas Map Ref 47 G1

886 St James Walkway Rest Area
Adjacent SH7, Lewis Pass

Map 16 C3

2459800E 5853600N
Hema Atlas Map Ref 47 F1

887 Riverside Rest Area
Adjacent SH7, Lewis Pass

Map 16 C3

2458900E 5857100N
Hema Atlas Map Ref 47 F1

888 Deer Hunters Flat
Adjacent SH7, Lewis Pass

Map 16 C3

2459700E 5859800N
Hema Atlas Map Ref 47 F1

889 Deer Valley
W of SH7: adjacent Lewis River
DoC Arthur's Pass Visitor Centre Ph (03) 318 9211
arthurspassvc@doc.govt.nz

Map 16 C3

Stream water only

2459700E 5867000N
Hema Atlas Map Ref 46 E13

890 Maruia Springs Thermal Resort
SH7: 15km SE of Springs Junction (SH65)
Ph/Fax (03) 523 8840 enquiries@maruiasprings.co.nz

Map 16 C3

Author's note - Although this is really more cabins than camping, camping options and spots for caravans are available. The surrounding mountains, beech forests and tussocks combine to make this a unique thermal pool experience.

2454500E 5870100N
Hema Atlas Map Ref 46 D13

891 Roadside Rest Area
SH7: SE of Springs Junction (SH65)

Map 16 C3

2447900E 5872900N
Hema Atlas Map Ref 46 D12

892

Map 16 C3

Marble Hill

SH7: 7km E of Springs Junction (SH65)
www.doc.govt.nz or Westport Visitor Centre
Ph (03) 789 6658 westport.info@xtra.co.nz
Access to the Lake Daniells Track.

2445200E 5873200N
Hema Atlas Map Ref 46 D12

893

Map 16 C3

Roadside Rest Area

SH7: at E edge of Springs Junction (SH65)

2443500E 5874600N
Hema Atlas Map Ref 46 D12

894

Map 16 C3

Roadside Rest Area

SH7: SE of Reefton

2421500E 5889500N
Hema Atlas Map Ref 46 C10

895

Map 16 C3

Roadside Rest Area

Inangahua Swingbridge Reserve, SH7: SE of Reefton

2421600E 5890700N
Hema Atlas Map Ref 46 B10

SH1 - Christchurch to Waipara

896

Map 17 AA1

Christchurch Top 10 Meadow Park Holiday Park

39 Meadow St, Papanui, Christchurch: signposted from
Main Nth Rd, just n of Northlands shopping centre
Ph (03) 352 9176 meadowpark@xtra.co.nz
Author's note - Top 10 seldom disappoint.

2478700E 5745800N
Hema Atlas Map Ref 120 E4, 56 D9

897

Map 17 AA1

219 on Johns' Motel & Holiday Park

219 Johns Rd, Belfast: alongside SH1 Christchurch
by-pass route S of Belfast
Ph (03) 323 8640 219johns@xtra.co.nz

2478100E 5750600N
Hema Atlas Map Ref 120 D5, 56 C9

898

Map 17 AA1

North South Holiday Park

Cnr of Johns (SH1) & Sawyers Arms Rds,
Harewood, Christchurch
Ph (03) 359 5993 northsouth@paradise.net.nz
Author's note - Handy to the Christchurch International Airport.

2475000E 5749400N
Hema Atlas Map Ref 120 C5, 56 D9

899

Map 17 AA2

Waimakariri River Rest Areas

On either bank of the River at major road crossings

Author's note - Popular fishing and boating spots for the locals.

2482100E 5755200N
Hema Atlas Map Ref 56 C10

900 Riverlands Holiday Park

Map 17 AA2

45 Doubledays Rd, Kaiapoi: signposted from
Old Main Rd 4km S of Kaiapoi
Ph (03) 327 5511 www.riverlandspark.co.nz
riverlandspark@xtra.co.nz

2482700E 5756500N

Hema Atlas Map Ref 56 C10

901 Blue Skies Training Centre & Camping Ground

Map 17 AA2

12 Williams St, Kaiapoi: adjacent old Main Rd, S of Kaiapoi
Ph (03) 327 8007 gary@blueskies.org.nz
Author's note - A Boy Scouts camp that is open to the public; offering
comprehensive facilities, including abseiling.

2482600E 5757700N
Hema Atlas Map Ref 56 C10

902 Kairaki Beach Holiday Park

Map 17 AA2

Featherston Ave, Kairaki Beach: signposted from
centre of Kaiapoi
Ph (03) 327 7335
Author's note - The many permanent residents offer incredible
'home and garden' displays, and there are opportunities for
swimming and walking on the nearby beach.

2486800E 5758100N
Hema Atlas Map Ref 56 C10

903 Rangiora Holiday Park

Map 16 E4
19 A7

337 Lehmans Rd, Rangiora: signposted off SH72
W of Rangiora, opposite the Racecourse
Ph/Fax (03) 313 5759 rangioraholidaypark@hotmail.com
Author's note - The very good facilities have attracted numerous
permanent residents.

2473900E 5767700N
Hema Atlas Map Ref 56 B9

904 Leigh Camp Holiday Park

16 E4 19 A7

N of Ashley, off Birch Hill Rd

A caretaker may collect fees if they are in attendance. Author's note
- Sheltered and sunny site, but basic.

2474000E 5771700N
Hema Atlas Map Ref 56 A9

905 Pineacres Holiday Park

16 E4 19 A7

740 Main North Rd: N of Kaiapoi on SH1
Ph (03) 327 5022 pineacres@xtra.co.nz

2482200E 5762500N
Hema Atlas Map Ref 56 B10

906 Woodend Beach Holiday Park

16 E4 19 A7

4km E of SH1 at Woodend Beach: follow the signs
from SH1
Ph (03) 312 7643 woodendbeach@xtra.co.nz
Author's note - Next to a lovely beach.

2486000E 5764100N
Hema Atlas Map Ref 56 B10

907 Waikuku Beach Holiday Park

16 E4 19 A8

5km E of SH1 at Waikuku: follow the signs from SH1
Ph/Fax (03) 312 7600 arkiwi@hotmail.com
Author's note - Neat facilities with swimming and walking
at the nearby beach.

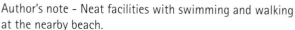

2487200E 5769700N
Hema Atlas Map Ref 56 B10

908
Map 16 D4

Leithfield Beach Motor Camp
18 Lucas Dr, Leithfield Beach: turn off SH1
at the Pukeko Junction Café
Ph/Fax (03) 314 3518 bryarlyn@xtra.co.nz
Author's note - Right next to the beach.

2490400E 5778000N
Hema Atlas Map Ref 56 A11

909
Map 16 D4

Delhaven Motels & Camping Ground
124 Carters Rd, Amberley: adjacent SH1 at
S end of Amberley
Ph (03) 314 8550 amberleydelhavenmotel@xtra.co.nz

2487300E 5783000N
Hema Atlas Map Ref 54 D8

910
Map 16 D4

Amberley Beach Reserve
Amberley Beach: 4km E of SH1

A caretaker may collect fees if they are in attendance. Author's note
- Simple, sheltered reserve that's handy to a nice beach.

2492600E 5782000N
Hema Atlas Map Ref 54 D9

SH73 - Christchurch to Greymouth

911
Map 17 AB1

Addington Park Accommodation and Camp
47-51 Whiteleigh Ave, Addington, Christchurch: follow
signs to Addington Park raceway
Ph (03) 338 9770 addacc@xtra.co.nz

2477600E 5741100N
Hema Atlas Map Ref 120 D2, 56 D9

912
Map 17 AB1

Amber Park Holiday Park
308 Blenheim Rd, Upper Riccarton
Ph/Fax (03) 348 3327 www.amberpark.co.nz
amberpark@xtra.co.nz
Author's note - A wee beauty - compact, neat and tidy.

2476300E 5741300N
Hema Atlas Map Ref 120 D2, 56 D9

913
Map 17 AB1

Riccarton Park Holiday Park
19 Main Sth Rd, Church Corner, Upper Riccarton
Ph (03) 348 5690 www.riccartonparkholidaypark.co.nz
csa@xtra.co.nz
Author's note - Older in style, but neat and tidy.

2475600E 5742400N
Hema Atlas Map Ref 120 C2, 56 D9

914
16 E3 19 A7

Glentunnel Holiday Park
Homebush Rd, Glentunnel: signposted from SH77
Ph (03) 318 2868 glentunnelholidaypark@xtra.co.nz

Author's note - Swimming in the adjoining Selwyn River.

2423700E 5746100N
Hema Atlas Map Ref 55 D4

915
16 E3 19 A7

Waimakariri River Rest Area
Adjacent SH72 (Waimakariri Gorge Rd): S side of river

Author's note - Fishing, canoeing and boating options abound.

2431600E 5760900N
Hema Atlas Map Ref 55 B5

916

Rest Area

Adjacent SH72: S of Oxford

16 E3 19 A7

2442100E 5767600N
Hema Atlas Map Ref 55 B6

917

Ashley Gorge Reserve Motor Camp

Ashley Gorge Rd, Ashley Gorge: 9km N of Oxford
Ph (03) 312 4099 bh.norton@clear.net.nz

Map 16 D3

2447400E 5775900N
Hema Atlas Map Ref 55 A6

918

Mt Thomas

Hayland Rd: 30km NW of Rangiora
DoC North Canterbury and Regional Visitor Information
Ph (03) 371 3706 northcantyvc@doc.govt.nz

Map 16 D3

2456800E 5779500N
Hema Atlas Map Ref 55 A7

919

Kowhai Pass Reserve

E end of Springfield: signposted from SH73

Author's note - Sheltered spot with tennis courts; well
worth checking out.

16 E3 19 A7

2424700E 5762900N
Hema Atlas Map Ref 55 B4

920

Rest Area

Adjacent SH73: W of Springfield

16 E3 19 A6

2412300E 5764500N
Hema Atlas Map Ref 55 B3

921

Lake Lyndon Rest Area

Adjacent SH73, Lake Lyndon

16 E3 19 A6

2404700E 5767400N
Hema Atlas Map Ref 55 B2

922

Cave Stream Scenic Reserve

Adjacent SH73: N of Castle Hill Village

Map 16 D3

2408300E 5779100N
Hema Atlas Map Ref 52 E9

923

Craigieburn, Craigieburn Conservation Park

Adjacent SH73, Craigieburn Conservation Park
DoC Arthur's Pass Visitor Centre Ph (03) 318 9211
arthurspassvc@doc.govt.nz

Map 16 D3

Stream water only Author's note - Favoured for walking
and mountain biking.

2406400E 5783900N
Hema Atlas Map Ref 52 D9

924

Flock Hill High Country Lodge

Adjacent SH73: S of Arthur's Pass
Ph (03) 318 8196 lodge@flockhill.co.nz

Author's note - A nice combination of high country
farming and camping.

Map 16 D3

2410300E 5784800N
Hema Atlas Map Ref 52 D10

925

Map 16 D3

Lake Pearson (Moana Rua)

Adjacent SH73, Lake Pearson: halfway between Springfield and Arthur's Pass
DoC Arthur's Pass Visitor Centre Ph (03) 318 9211
arthurspassvc@doc.govt.nz
Stream water only

2411200E 5790400N
Hema Atlas Map Ref 52 C10

926

Map 16 D3

Andrews Shelter, Arthur's Pass National Park

5km along Mt White Rd: off SH73
DoC Arthur's Pass Visitor Centre Ph (03) 318 9211
arthurspassvc@doc.govt.nz
Stream water only

2412300E 5800200N
Hema Atlas Map Ref 52 B10

927

Map 16 D3

Hawdon, Arthur's Pass National Park

Lower Hawdon Valley, Arthurs Pass National Park
DoC Arthur's Pass Visitor Centre Ph (03) 318 9211
arthurspassvc@doc.govt.nz
Stream water only

2407900E 5802000N
Hema Atlas Map Ref 52 B9

928

Map 16 D2

Klondyke Corner, Arthur's Pass National Park

Adjacent SH73, 8km S of Arthur's Pass
DoC Arthur's Pass Visitor Centre Ph (03) 318 9211
arthurspassvc@doc.govt.nz
Stream water only; no fires

2394100E 5799900N
Hema Atlas Map Ref 52 B8

929

Map 16 D2

Greyney Shelter, Arthur's Pass National Park

Adjacent SH73, 5km E of Arthur's Pass
DoC Arthur's Pass Visitor Centre Ph (03) 318 9211
arthurspassvc@doc.govt.nz
Stream water only

2394200E 5801500N
Hema Atlas Map Ref 52 B8

930

Map 16 D2

Avalanche Creek (Arthur's Pass), Arthur's Pass National Park

Opposite the DoC Information Centre, Arthur's Pass
DoC Arthur's Pass Visitor Centre Ph (03) 318 9211
arthurspassvc@doc.govt.nz
Author's note - Casual camping right next to the town (and rail yards).

2393200E 5807300N
Hema Atlas Map Ref 52 B8

931

Map 16 D2

Roadside Rest Area

Temple Basin Skifield carpark: adjacent SH73,
W of Arthur's Pass

2393100E 5810400N
Hema Atlas Map Ref 52 A8

932

Map 16 D2

Roadside Rest Area

Deaths Corner, SH73: near the summit of Arthurs Pass (923m)

2391300E 5812100N
Hema Atlas Map Ref 52 A8

933

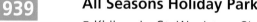

Otira Viaduct Lookout

Adjacent SH73, N of Arthur's Pass

Map 16 D2

2392800E 5813500N
Hema Atlas Map Ref 52 A8

934

Otira Hotel Campsite

Opposite Otira Hotel: adjacent SH73, Otira
Ph (03) 738 2890

Author's note - Traditional West Coast camping, that is basic
and best suited to campervans.

Map 16 D2

2393300E 5818800N
Hema Atlas Map Ref 52 A8

935

Kellys Creek Shelter

SH73: 17km N of Arthur's Pass
DoC Arthur's Pass Visitor Centre Ph (03) 318 9211
arthurspassvc@doc.govt.nz
Stream water only

Map 16 D2

2394000E 5821200N
Hema Atlas Map Ref 45 J7

936

Roadside Rest Area

The Avenue Scenic Reserve, SH73: W of Jacksons
DoC Arthur's Pass Visitor Centre Ph (03) 318 9211
arthurspassvc@doc.govt.nz

Map 16 D2

2387100E 5828900N
Hema Atlas Map Ref 45 J6

937

Roadside Rest Area

Adjacent SH73: W of Jacksons

Map 16 D2

2381400E 5829600N
Hema Atlas Map Ref 45 J6

938

Roadside Rest Area

Okuku Scenic Reserve, SH73: W of Turiwhate
DoC Arthur's Pass Visitor Centre Ph (03) 318 9211
arthurspassvc@doc.govt.nz

Map 16 D2

2366800E 5831600N
Hema Atlas Map Ref 45 H4

Banks Peninsula - Christchurch to Akaroa

939

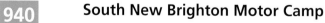

All Seasons Holiday Park

5 Kidbrooke St, Woolston, Christchurch: signposted
off Linwood Rd
Ph (03) 384 9490

Author's note - Handy to Sumner Beach.

Map 17 AB2

2485200E 5740800N
Hema Atlas Map Ref 120 G2, 56 D10

940

South New Brighton Motor Camp

Halsey St, South New Brighton, Christchurch:
signposted from Estuary Rd
Ph/Fax (03) 388 9844

Author's note - A typical beach camping ground, with walks and swimming opportunities, yet only 20 minutes from Christchurch city centre.

Map 17 AB2

2488400E 5741400N
Hema Atlas Map Ref 120 H2, 56 D10

941 — Map 17 AB2

Sumner Beach Reserve
Waterfront, Sumner, Christchurch

2490800E 5738400N
Hema Atlas Map Ref 120 H1, 56 E11

---

942 — Map 17 AB2

Mt Cavendish Scenic Reserve
Summit Rd, Heathcote Valley, Christchurch

2486900E 5734700N
Hema Atlas Map Ref 56 E10

---

943 — Map 17 AB2

Coronation Hill Reserve/Sign of the Kiwi Rest Area
Dyers Pass Rd, Christchurch

2480800E 5734000N
Hema Atlas Map Ref 56 E10

---

944 — Map 17 AB2

Allendale Reserve
Governors Bay, Christchurch

2482400E 5730100N
Hema Atlas Map Ref 56 E10

---

945 — Map 17 AB2

Charteris Bay Reserve
Marine Dr, Charteris Bay, Christchurch

2485300E 5728500N
Hema Atlas Map Ref 56 F10

---

946 — Map 17 AB2

Purau Bay Holiday Park
Purau Bay: 2km SE of Diamond Harbour, Banks Peninsula
Ph 0800 468 678 puraubay@xtra.co.nz
Author's note - Pleasant surroundings with opportunities for swimming and boating.

2490300E 5730400N
Hema Atlas Map Ref 56 E11

---

947 — 16 E4 19 A7

Gebbies Pass Summit
Akaroa end of Summit Rd, Banks Peninsula

2481800E 5723300N
Hema Atlas Map Ref 56 F10

---

948 — 16 E4 19 A8

French Farm Rest Area
Wainui Main Rd, French Farm, Banks Peninsula: S of SH75

2502100E 5715000N
Hema Atlas Map Ref 56 G12

---

949 — 16 E4 19 A8

YMCA Wainui Park
Wainui Valley Rd, Wainui, Banks Peninsula
Ph (03) 304 8460 wainui@ymcachch.org.nz
Author's note - Canoeing and highwire facilities.
Bookings recommended.

2502000E 5711300N
Hema Atlas Map Ref 56 G12

950

Duvauchelle Bay Rest Area

SH75, Duvauchelle Bay, Banks Peninsula

16 E4 19 A8

2503900E 5718200N

Hema Atlas Map Ref 56 G12

951

Duvauchelle Holiday Park

Seafield Rd, Duvauchelle, Banks Peninsula:
clearly visible from SH75
Ph (03) 304 5777 duvauchelleholidaypark@hotmail.com
Author's note - Exposed but harbourside.

16 E4 19 A8

2504900E 5716300N

Hema Atlas Map Ref 56 G12

952

Akaroa Top 10 Holiday Park

96 Morgans Rd, Akaroa, Banks Peninsula: signposted from
main road into Akaroa, and from Akaroa Centre
Ph (03) 304 7471 holidaypark@xtra.co.nz
Author's note - Sheltered spot with charming views that's handy to
Akaroa town centre.

Map 16 E4
19 A8

2506600E 5712800N

Hema Atlas Map Ref 56 G12

953

Akaroa Domain Rest Area

Akaroa Domain, Akaroa, Banks Peninsula

16 E4 19 A8

2508400E 5711700N

Hema Atlas Map Ref 56 G12

954

Le Bons Bay Motor Camp

15 Valley Rd, Le Bons Bay, Banks Peninsula: off Summit Rd
Ph (03) 304 8533

16 E4 19 A8

2513500E 5716000N

Hema Atlas Map Ref 56 G13

955

Okains Bay Camping Ground

1162 Okains Bay Rd, Okains Bay, Banks Peninsula: 13km
from Akaroa Rd, via Summit Rd
Ph (03) 304 8789

16 E4 19 A8

A caretaker may collect fees if they are in attendance.
Author's note - Take care on the twisty access road. The Okains Bay
museum is well worth a visit.

2514600E 5723900N

Hema Atlas Map Ref 56 F13

SH1 - Christchurch to Ashburton

956

Alpine View Holiday Park

650 Main South Rd (SH1), Templeton, Christchurch
Ph (03) 349 7666 alpine.view@xtra.co.nz
Author's note - Functional, but not memorable.

Map 17 AB1

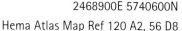

2468900E 5740600N

Hema Atlas Map Ref 120 A2, 56 D8

957

Rest Area

Adjacent SH1 at both ends of the Rakaia bridge

16 E3 19 A7

2432500E 5719100N

Hema Atlas Map Ref 55 G5

958

Rakaia River Holiday Park

Main South Rd (SH1), Rakaia: S end of Rakaia bridge
Ph/Fax (03) 302 7546

16 E3 19 A7   Author's note - Situated next to a major salmon-fishing river.

2431300E 5717600N

Hema Atlas Map Ref 55 G5

959

Rakaia Huts Camping Area

At N mouth of Rakaia River: 30km SE of SH1
Ashburton District Council 'Freedom Camping'
www.ashburtondc.govt.nz

16 E3 19 A7   A caretaker may collect fees if they are in attendance.
Author's note - Regarded as a favoured spot for keen salmon anglers.

2449300E 5702900N

Hema Atlas Map Ref 55 H6

960

Rest Area

Adjacent SH1, at intersection with Sommerton Rd: S of
Rakaia, N of Ashburton

16 E3 19 A7

2417300E 5708100N

Hema Atlas Map Ref 55 H3

961

Coronation Holiday Park

778 East St, Ashburton: adjacent SH1 at N end
of Ashburton
Ph (03) 308 6603 dalbar@ihug.co.nz

16 E3 19 A6   Author's note - Spa pool to ease the aches.

2411000E 5700000N

Hema Atlas Map Ref 55 J3

962

Rest Area

SH1: either end of the bridge at the S end of Ashburton

16 E3 19 A6

2408300E 5699800N

Hema Atlas Map Ref 55 J2

963

Methven Camping Grounds

Barkers Rd, Methven: SH77, N of Ashburton,
S of Mount Hutt
Ph (03) 302 8005 methvennz@hotmail.co.nz

16 E3 19 A6   Author's note - Spacious parklike grounds.

2401700E 5730500N

Hema Atlas Map Ref 55 E2

964

Pudding Hill Lodge

SH72 Pudding Hill: SW of Mount Hutt, NW of Methven
Ph (03) 302 9627 www.puddinghilllodge.co.nz

Map 16 E2
19 A6

2391000E 5735000N

Hema Atlas Map Ref 52 J8

SH1 - Ashburton to Timaru

965

Ashburton Holiday Park

Tinwald Domain, Moronan Rd, Tinwald: W from SH1,
S of Tinwald township
Ph/Fax (03) 308 6805 pat.sue@xtra.co.nz

Map 16 E3
19 A6   Author's note - Set in mature, parklike grounds, adjoining tennis
courts and duck pond.

2405400E 5697500N

Hema Atlas Map Ref 62 D8

966
Map 19 B6

Orari Bridge Holiday Park
Cnr Keen Rd & SH 72/79: 6km N of Geraldine
Ph/Fax (03) 693 7453

2370500E 5683700N
Hema Atlas Map Ref 61 E5

967
Map 19 B6

Arundel Bridge Reserve
S end of Arundel Bridge, SH72

2372900E 5692000N
Hema Atlas Map Ref 61 D5

968
Map 16 E2
19 A6

Peel Forest Park
Peel Forest: off SH72, 12km NW of Arundel
Register at Peel Forest Shop before camping Ph (03) 696 3567;
DoC North Canterbury and Regional Visitor
Information Ph (03) 371 3706 northcantyvc@doc.govt.nz

2371300E 5700700N
Hema Atlas Map Ref 61 C5

969
Map 19 B6

Orari Gorge
Yates Rd: 12km NW of Geraldine, via Tripp Settlement
DoC North Canterbury and Regional Visitor Information
Ph (03) 371 3706 northcantyvc@doc.govt.nz

2363100E 5689600N
Hema Atlas Map Ref 61 E4

970
Map 19 B6

Waihi Gorge
Waihi Gorge Rd: 14km NW of Geraldine, beside Waihi River
DoC North Canterbury and Regional Visitor Information
Ph (03) 371 3706 northcantyvc@doc.govt.nz

2360400E 5687400N
Hema Atlas Map Ref 61 E4

971
Map 19 B6

Geraldine Holiday Park
39 Hislop St, Geraldine: signposted from SH72
& SH79 in town centre
Ph/Fax (03) 693 8147 geraldineholidaypark@xtra.co.nz

2368600E 5678400N
Hema Atlas Map Ref 61 F4

972
Map 19 B6

Winchester Motor Camp
Adjacent SH1, Winchester: S end of town

A caretaker may collect fees if they are in attendance. Author's note
- Simple but all the basics are here.

972 2373100E 5666600N
Hema Atlas Map Ref 61 G5

973
Map 19 B6

Temuka Holiday Park
Fergusson Dr, Temuka: signposted E from
Temuka town centre
Ph (03) 615 7241
Author's note - An unexpected treat.

2373200E 5661500N
Hema Atlas Map Ref 61 G5

974
Map 19 B6

Riverside Rest Area
Adjacent SH1, S of Temuka

2371300E 5659800N
Hema Atlas Map Ref 61 H5

975 Timaru Top 10 Holiday Park

Map 19 B6

154 Selwyn St, Timaru: located off Hobbs St,
adjoining Pak-n-Save
Ph (03) 684 7690 or 0800 242 121
topten@timaruholidaypark.co.nz
Author's note - Just 1km from the beach and town centre.

2368700E 5646100N
Hema Atlas Map Ref 61 J4

976 Caroline Bay Beach Rest Area

Map 19 B6

Caroline Bay Park: signposted from Timaru town centre

$

2370800E 5645700N
Hema Atlas Map Ref 121 B2, 61 J5

977 Glenmark Motor Camp

Map 19 B6

Beaconsfield Rd, Timaru: signposted from
SH1 at S end of Timaru
Ph/Fax (03) 684 3682 glenparkmotorcamp@xtra.co.nz

2369300E 5642500N
Hema Atlas Map Ref 61 J4

SH8 - Timaru to Twizel

978 Cave Rest Area

Map 19 B6

Adjacent SH8: 16km W of Pleasant Point, 29km S of Fairlie

$

2346500E 5654100N
Hema Atlas Map Ref 61 H2

979 Mt Nimrod

Map 19 B5

Back Line Rd: 32km SW of Timaru, via Motukaika
DoC North Canterbury and Regional Visitor Information
Ph (03) 371 3706 northcantyvc@doc.govt.nz

2340400E 5638900N
Hema Atlas Map Ref 61 J2

980 Rest Area

Map 19 B6

Adjacent SH8: S Fairlie

2340400E 5665000N
Hema Atlas Map Ref 61 G2

981 Fairlie Gateway Top 10 Motor Camp

Map 19 B5

10 Allandale Rd, Fairlie: SH79 signposted from
the centre of Fairlie
Ph/Fax (03) 685 8375 or 0800 324 754
relax@fairlietop10.co.nz
Author's not - Peaceful parklike surroundings.

2336500E 5677600N
Hema Atlas Map Ref 61 F1

982 Pioneer Park

Map 19 B6

Homebush Rd: 14km W of Geraldine,
via Gudex/Middle Valley roads
DoC North Canterbury and Regional Visitor Information
Ph (03) 371 3706 northcantyvc@doc.govt.nz

2345800E 5672200N
Hema Atlas Map Ref 61 F2

983

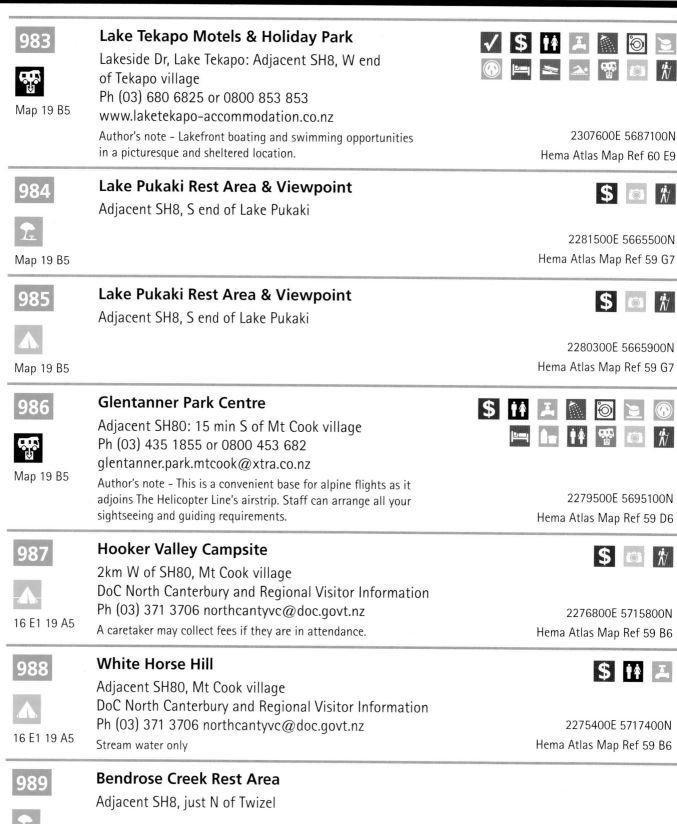

Map 19 B5

Lake Tekapo Motels & Holiday Park

Lakeside Dr, Lake Tekapo: Adjacent SH8, W end
of Tekapo village
Ph (03) 680 6825 or 0800 853 853
www.laketekapo-accommodation.co.nz

Author's note - Lakefront boating and swimming opportunities
in a picturesque and sheltered location.

2307600E 5687100N
Hema Atlas Map Ref 60 E9

984

Map 19 B5

Lake Pukaki Rest Area & Viewpoint

Adjacent SH8, S end of Lake Pukaki

2281500E 5665500N
Hema Atlas Map Ref 59 G7

985

Map 19 B5

Lake Pukaki Rest Area & Viewpoint

Adjacent SH8, S end of Lake Pukaki

2280300E 5665900N
Hema Atlas Map Ref 59 G7

986

Map 19 B5

Glentanner Park Centre

Adjacent SH80: 15 min S of Mt Cook village
Ph (03) 435 1855 or 0800 453 682
glentanner.park.mtcook@xtra.co.nz

Author's note - This is a convenient base for alpine flights as it
adjoins The Helicopter Line's airstrip. Staff can arrange all your
sightseeing and guiding requirements.

2279500E 5695100N
Hema Atlas Map Ref 59 D6

987

16 E1 19 A5

Hooker Valley Campsite

2km W of SH80, Mt Cook village
DoC North Canterbury and Regional Visitor Information
Ph (03) 371 3706 northcantyvc@doc.govt.nz

A caretaker may collect fees if they are in attendance.

2276800E 5715800N
Hema Atlas Map Ref 59 B6

988

16 E1 19 A5

White Horse Hill

Adjacent SH80, Mt Cook village
DoC North Canterbury and Regional Visitor Information
Ph (03) 371 3706 northcantyvc@doc.govt.nz

Stream water only

2275400E 5717400N
Hema Atlas Map Ref 59 B6

989

Map 19 B5

Bendrose Creek Rest Area

Adjacent SH8, just N of Twizel

2279000E 5658100N
Hema Atlas Map Ref 59 H6

990

Map 19 B5

Parklands Alpine Tourist Park

122 Mackenzie Dr, Twizel
Ph (03) 435 0507 parklands1@xtra.co.nz

2277800E 5657300N
Hema Atlas Map Ref 59 H6

991 Lake Ruataniwha Holiday Park

Max Smith Dr, Twizel: about 5km W of Twizel,
signposted from SH8 at S end of Twizel
Ph (03) 435 0613 holidaypark2000@xtra.co.nz

Author's note - Handy to the South Island's best rowing venue,
with fishing, boating and safe swimming at your back door.

Map 19 B5

2275100E 5656100N
Hema Atlas Map Ref 59 H6

992 Lake Ruataniwha Recreation Reserve

Adjacent SH8, S of Twizel

Map 19 B5

2278400E 5654200N
Hema Atlas Map Ref 59 H6

993 Lake Wairepo Rest Area

Adjacent SH8, S of Twizel

Map 19 B5

2275400E 5652700N
Hema Atlas Map Ref 59 H6

994 Lake Ohau and Lake Middleton Recreation Reserves

17km NW of SH8: turn off SH8 13km S of Twizel

Map 18 B4   A caretaker may collect fees if they are in attendance.

2258000E 5653000N
Hema Atlas Map Ref 59 H4

995 Temple Forest

Lake Ohau Rd: 18km N of Lake Ohau Alpine Village
DoC North Canterbury and Regional Visitor Information
Ph (03) 371 3706 northcantyvc@doc.govt.nz

Map 18 B4   Stream water only

2256300E 5672800N
Hema Atlas Map Ref 59 F4

SH1 - Timaru to Oamaru

996 Otaio Gorge

Back Line Rd: 29km SW of Timaru, via Gordons Valley
DoC North Canterbury and Regional Visitor Information
Ph (03) 371 3706 northcantyvc@doc.govt.nz

Map 19 B6

2345400E 5628900N
Hema Atlas Map Ref 68 B11

997 St Andrews Recreation Reserve & Camping Ground

Adjacent SH1, S end of Saint Andrews

Map 19 B6   A caretaker may collect fees if they are in attendance.

2366200E 5628100N
Hema Atlas Map Ref 68 B13

998 Victoria Park Camp & Cabins

Cnr Tennant & Naylor Sts, Waimate: at S end of Waimate
Ph (03) 689 8079

Author's note - Good facilities in a parklike setting, and handy
to the town centre.

Map 19 C6

2354000E 5605800N
Hema Atlas Map Ref 68 D12

999

Map 19 C6

Knottingley Park Motor Camp

Waihao Back Rd, Waimate: at S end of Waimate

Ph (03) 689 8079 graeme@waimatedc.govt.nz

Author's note – Peaceful and reasonably priced with 'character' facilities in a magnificent 36ha forest park.

2355600E 5604300N

Hema Atlas Map Ref 68 D12

1000

Map 19 C6

Kelceys Bush Farmyard & Holiday Park

Mill Rd: 12 km inland from Waimate

Ph (03) 689 8057 kelceysbush@xtra.co.nz

Author's note – An opportunity to get up close and personal with a range of NZ wildlife and farm animals in a pretty valley setting.

2349100E 5610300N

Hema Atlas Map Ref 68 C11

1001

Map 19 C6

Rest Area

SH82: S of Waimate, W of Glenavy

2342900E 5589900N

Hema Atlas Map Ref 68 F11

1002

Map 19 C6

Gateways Caravan Park

Main Rd, Glenavy

Ph (03) 689 3875 Fax (03) 689 3872

Author's note – A favoured salmon and trout fishing base.

2360800E 5586600N

Hema Atlas Map Ref 68 F13

1003

Map 19 C6

Waitaki River Rest Area

Adjacent SH1: at N end of Waitaki River bridge

$

2360800E 5585400N

Hema Atlas Map Ref 68 F13

104

Map 19 C6

Waitaki Mouth Motor Camp

305 Kaik Rd, Waitaki: E off SH1, just S of the Waitaki River bridge

Ph/Fax (03) 431 3880 waitakimouth@kol.co.nz

Author's note – Ideal for anglers seeking salmon and trout from the nearby Waitaki River.

2362400E 5582900N

Hema Atlas Map Ref 68 F13

Shags, Oamaru. Photo Donna Blaber

south island camping sites

Queenstown

OTAGO REGION

SH83 - SH1 to Omarama (SH8)

1005 — **Danseys Pass Holiday Park**

Dansey's Pass Rd: 15km S of Duntroon, SH83
Ph (03) 431 2564 Fax (03) 431 2560
Author's note - A magic and tranquil spot, with opportunities for gold panning or swimming in the Maerewhenua River. It's also a convenient base from which to explore the Vanished World fossil trail.
 Map 19 C5
2318300E 5582500N
Hema Atlas Map Ref 68 F8

1006 — **Kurow Holiday Park**

76 Bledisloe St, Kurow: adjacent SH83 at NW end of Kurow
Ph (03) 436 0725 winskurow@xtra.co.nz
Author's note - Located on the south bank of the Waitaki River, with freshwater swimming and fishing at your backdoor
 Map 19 C5
2309000E 5606600N
Hema Atlas Map Ref 67 D7

1007 — **Hakataramea Rest Area**
Adjacent SH82: N side of Waitaki R
 Map 19 C5
2310200E 5606800N
Hema Atlas Map Ref 68 D8

1008 — **Aviemore Dam & Fishermans Bend Recreation Reserve**

N side of Lake Aviemore: off SH83
A caretaker may collect fees if they are in attendance. Author's note - Numerous casual camping, boat launching, picnicking and fishing sites that are well worth exploring.
 Map 19 C5
2301200E 5614100N
Hema Atlas Map Ref 67 C7

1009 — **Parsons Creek Recreation Reserve**
Adjacent SH83: S side of Lake Aviemore
A caretaker may collect fees if they are in attendance. Author's note - Lakeside swimming, fishing and boating opportunities.
 Map 19 C5
2290700E 5616600N
Hema Atlas Map Ref 67 C6

1010 — **Otematata Holiday Park**

East Rd, Otematata: S of SH83
Ph/Fax (03) 438 7826
 Map 19 B5
2287500E 5618100N
Hema Atlas Map Ref 67 C5

SOUTH ISLAND

1011

Map 19 B5

Benmore Dam Recreation Reserve

N of SH83 from Otematata

A caretaker may collect fees if they are in attendance. Author's note - Follow this road for a scenic drive to Aviemore with plentiful lakeside camping, swimming, fishing and boating opportunities.

2287600E 5619700N
Hema Atlas Map Ref 67 C5

1012

Map 19 B5

Loch Laird Recreation Reserve

Adjacent SH83 and Lake Benmore

A caretaker may collect fees if they are in attendance.

2278100E 5622000N
Hema Atlas Map Ref 67 B4

1013

Map 19 B5

Sailors Cutting Recreation Reserve

Adjacent SH83 and Lake Benmore

A caretaker may collect fees if they are in attendance.

2279000E 5625600N
Hema Atlas Map Ref 67 B4

1014

Map 19 B5

Lake Benmore Holiday Park

Adjacent SH83 and Lake Benmore: 7km E of Omarama
Ph/Fax (03) 438 9624 benmoreview@xtra.co.nz

Author's note - Campers have access to the lake edge for boating, fishing and swimming. Each site even has its own personal toilet and shower!

2276400E 5628200N
Hema Atlas Map Ref 67 B4

SH1 - Omaru to Palmerston

1015

Map 19 C6

Oamaru Top 10 Holiday Park

Chelmer St, Oamaru: adjoining Oamaru's Botanic Gardens
Ph (03) 434 7666 or 0800 28 02 02
oamarutop10@xtra.co.nz

Author's note - Sheltered site with pretty walks.

2349100E 5566500N
Hema Atlas Map Ref 68 H11

1016

Map 19 C6

Kakanui Camping Ground

14km S of Oamaru on Coast Rd

A caretaker may collect fees if they are in attendance.

2344800E 5555600N
Hema Atlas Map Ref 68 J11

1017

Map 19 C6

All Day Bay Recreation Reserve

All Day Bay, Coast Rd: S of Kakanui

2344200E 5553700N
Hema Atlas Map Ref 68 J11

1018

Map 19 C5

Glencoe Reserve

2km W of Herbert: off SH1
DoC Coastal Otago Visitor Centre (03) 477 0677

2333300E 5550500N
Hema Atlas Map Ref 68 J10

1019 🏕 Map 19 C5

Olive Grove Holiday Park

Waianakarua: adjacent SH1, 28km S of Oamaru

A caretaker may collect fees if they are in attendance.
Author's note - Relaxed rural ambiance with stream for bathing and/or swimming.

2337600E 5548700N
Hema Atlas Map Ref 68 A13

1020 🚐 Map 19 C5

Hampden Beach Motor Camp

2 Carlisle St, Hampden: E of SH1, 35km S of Oamaru
Ph (03) 439 4439

Author's note - Sheltered scenic beachside camp.

2339900E 5539600N
Hema Atlas Map Ref 74 B13

1021 🚐 Map 19 D6

Moeraki Motor Camp

114 Haven St, Moeraki: E of SH1, 40km S of Oamaru
Ph/Fax (03) 439 4759 moerakimotorcamp@xtra.co.nz
Author's note - Scenic coastal fishing village with a great local seafood restaurant in Fleurs Café.

2341000E 5536800N
Hema Atlas Map Ref 74 B14

1022 🌲 Map 19 D5

Trotters Gorge Scenic Reserve

Turn off SH1 2km S of Moeraki or just N of Palmerston

2336500E 5532200N
Hema Atlas Map Ref 74 B13

1023 🏕 Map 19 D5

Shag Point Recreation Reserve

Off SH1 near Shag Point: 10km N of Palmerston
or 61km S of Oamaru
DoC Coastal Otago Visitor Centre (03) 477 0677

2339100E 5523900N
Hema Atlas Map Ref 74 C13

SH85 - Palmerston to Alexandra

1024 🌲 Map 19 D5

Roadside Rest Area

Shag River swimming hole: adjacent SH85,
NW of Palmerston

Author's note - Favoured local swimming and picnic spot.

2326100E 5531300N
Hema Atlas Map Ref 74 B12

1025 🌲 Map 19 C5

Roadside Rest Area

Pigroot Creek, adjacent SH85: SE of Kyeburn

2308100E 5554200N
Hema Atlas Map Ref 67 J7

1026 🌲 Map 19 D5

Otago Central Rail Trail Memorial Rest Area

Adjacent SH87: S of Hyde, N of Middlemarch

2291700E 5535400N
Hema Atlas Map Ref 74 B9

1027 Dansey Pass Hotel

Map 19 C5

Dansey's Pass Rd: N of SH85 from Kyeburn

Author's note - Dansey's Pass Rd is not recommended for bigger campers and buses: treat this road with respect.

2295300E 5577400N
Hema Atlas Map Ref 67 G6

1028 Ranfurly Motor Camp

Map 19 C5

3 Reade St, Ranfurly: signposted from the centre of Ranfurly
Ph/Fax (03) 444 9144

Author's note - A convenient base for the Ranfurly to Middlemarch stage of the Otago Central Rail Trail.

2282700E 5560700N
Hema Atlas Map Ref 67 H5

1029 Larchview Camping Grounds

Map 19 C5

Swimming Dam Rd, Naseby: signposted from Naseby centre
Ph/Fax (03) 444 9904

Author's note - Set in a pretty former goldmining town, this camp is handy to mountainbiking trails and a dam for ice skating and curling in winter.

2284100E 5572000N
Hema Atlas Map Ref 67 G5

1030 Wedderburn Roadside Rest Area

Map 19 C5

SH85: rest area for the Central Otago Rail Trail

2274500E 5571800N
Hema Atlas Map Ref 67 G4

1031 Roadside Rest Area

Map 18 C4

Hills Creek, adjacent SH85

2266400E 5579100N
Hema Atlas Map Ref 67 G3

1032 Blue Lake Recreation Reserve

Map 18 C4

St Bathans: a 10km diversion N of SH85

Author's note - A beautiful picnic spot in an intriguing old gold town.

2258400E 5588800N
Hema Atlas Map Ref 67 F2

1033 Lauder Roadside Rest Area

Map 18 C4

SH85: rest area for the Central Otago Rail Trail

2247400E 5568300N
Hema Atlas Map Ref 67 H1

1034 Omakau Recreation Reserve Camping Ground

Map 18 C4

Signposted W off SH85 at the S end of Omakau

A caretaker may collect fees or donations.

2241500E 5562800N
Hema Atlas Map Ref 66 H12

1035 Alexandra Tourist Park

Map 18 C4

31 Ngapara St, Alexandra: signposted off SH85,
N of Alexandra
Ph (03) 448 8861 alex.touristpark@xtra.co.nz

Author's note - Only 250m from the Central Otago Rail Trail.

2227100E 5545800N
Hema Atlas Map Ref 73 A2

1036

Map 18 C4

Alexandra Holiday Park

Manuherikia Rd, Alexandra: off SH85, N of Alexandra
Ph (03) 448 8297 alex.hol.park@xtra.co.nz
Author's note - A very popular camp with swimming in
the adjoining river.

2227100E 5545800N

Hema Atlas Map Ref 73 A2

SH1 - Palmerston to Dunedin

1037

Map 19 D5

Waikouaiti Beach Motor Camp

186 Beach St, Waikouaiti: E from SH1,
S edge of Waikouaiti township
Ph (03) 465 7340

2328500E 5508900N

Hema Atlas Map Ref 74 E12

1038

Map 19 D5

Karitane Caravan Park

123 Stornoway St, Karitane: 3km E of SH1, 56 km N of
Dunedin
A caretaker may collect fees if they are in attendance.
Author's note - Scenic beach site, with a Maori Pa site nearby.

2327600E 5505500N

Hema Atlas Map Ref 74 E12

1039

Map 19 D5

Warrington Beach Domain

Warrington Domain, Esplanade, Warrington: 4km E of SH1
from Evansdale, 25km N of Dunedin
A caretaker may collect fees if they are in attendance. Author's note
- Scenic beachside location.

2322500E 5496200N

Hema Atlas Map Ref 74 F12

1040

Map 19 D5

Leith Valley Touring Park

103 Malvern St, Dunedin: off George St
Ph (03) 467 9936 lvtpdun@southnet.co.nz

2315700E 5481500N

Hema Atlas Map Ref 124 D3, 74 G11

1041

Map 19 D5

3 Mile Hill Rest Area & View Point

Three Mile Hill Rd: follow Stuart St up the hills from
the top of the Octagon
Author's note - On the most scenic route from Dunedin to Outram and
SH87 to Middlemarch. Extensive views of the Taieri Plains, yet only five
minutes from Dunedin's city centre.

2310700E 5481700N

Hema Atlas Map Ref 124 F3, 74 G11

1042

Map 19 D5

Aromoana (Pathway to the Sea)

Western entrance to Otago Harbour: 24km N of Dunedin
via Port Chalmers & SH 88
A caretaker may collect fees if they are in attendance.

2331800E 5490300N

Hema Atlas Map Ref 74 F13

1043

Map 19 D5

Vauxhall Reserve

Portobello Rd, Otago Peninsula

Day parking only

2317500E 5477600N

Hema Atlas Map Ref 124 D4, 74 H11

1044   Dunedin Holiday Park

Map 19 D5

41 Victoria Rd, St Kilda, Dunedin
Ph (03) 455 4690
office@dunedinholidaypark.co.nz

2317000E 5475300N
Hema Atlas Map Ref 124 D5, 74 H11

1045   Macandrew Bay Rest Area & Reserve

Map 19 D5

Portobello Rd, Macandrew Bay, Otago Peninsula

Author's note - Harbourside swimming and sunbathing adjoining
Macandrew Bay village.

2322800E 5479800N
Hema Atlas Map Ref 124 B3, 74 H12

1046   Portobello Village Tourist Park

Map 19 D5

27 Hereweka St, Portobello: E from centre
of Portobello village
Ph (03) 478 0359 portobellopark@xtra.co.nz

Author's note - Peaceful and sheltered spot, yet only 500m
from Portobello village.

2326800E 5483300N
Hema Atlas Map Ref 124 A2, 74 G12

SH1 - Dunedin to Milton

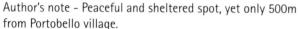

1047   Aaron Lodge

Map 19 D5

162 Kaikorai Valley Rd, Burnside, Dunedin:
3km from Dunedin City Centre
Ph (03) 476 4725 stay@aaronlodge.co.nz

2313700E 5476800N
Hema Atlas Map Ref 124 E3, 74 H11

1048   Mosgiel Motor Camp

Map 19 D5

221 Gordon Rd, Mosgiel

A caretaker may collect fees if they are in attendance.
Author's note - A small compact site akin to a permanent 'caravan park'.

2304300E 5479400N
Hema Atlas Map Ref 124 H4, 74 H10

1049   Outram Glen Picnic Area

Map 19 D5

Taieri Gorge/Outram Glen Scenic Reserve: turn N at the W
end of the Taieri River Bridge just 1km N of Outram

Author's note - A favourite summer swimming spot for local families.

2296200E 5480900N
Hema Atlas Map Ref 74 G9

1050   Blind Billy's Holiday Camp

Map 19 D5

Mold St, Middlemarch: signposted from the town centre
Ph (03) 464 3355 blindbillys@xtra.co.nz

Author's note - A handy base for the start/finish of the
Otago Central Rail Trail

2285900E 5517700N
Hema Atlas Map Ref 74 D8

1051   Brighton Motor Camp & Boat Hire

Map 19 D5

1044 Brighton Rd, Brighton: 24km S of Dunedin
on coastal route
Ph (03) 481 1404
Author's note - Close to an attractive sheltered beach.

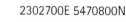

2302700E 5470800N
Hema Atlas Map Ref 124 J6, 74 H10

1052

Brighton Domain

Brighton Domain, Brighton: across the bridge
at S end of township

Map 19 D5 Author's note - Numerous beachside spots south of here.

2302500E 5469200N
Hema Atlas Map Ref 124 J6, 74 J10

1053

Taieri River Scenic Reserve (AKA Kaarston Park)

24km E of SH1 at Waihola or 40km S of Dunedin
on coastal route

Map 19 E5 Author's note - Favoured launching spot for coastal and river fishing.

2293500E 5458000N
Hema Atlas Map Ref 79 C7

1054

East Taieri Roadside Rest Area

SH1: 14km S of Dunedin, just S of turnoff
to Dunedin Airport

Map 19 D5 Author's note - Sheltered with picnic tables.

2297900E 5472000N
Hema Atlas Map Ref 79 B6

1055

Lake Waihola Holiday Park & Recreation Reserve

Waihola Domain, Waihola: W from SH1 in the centre
of Waihola township
Ph (03) 417 8908

Map 19 D5 Author's note - A favoured lakeside picnic spot that's popular
for boating and jet skiing.

2285600E 5461600N
Hema Atlas Map Ref 79 B6

1056

Sinclair Wetlands Camp

Clarendon-Berwick Rd, Berwick: W from SH1
either N or S of Waihola
Ph (03) 486 2654

Map 19 D5 Author's note - An eco-camp/lodge offering a small area for
campervans and camping with an opportunity to explore the
adjoining wildlife and wetlands reserve.

2282800E 5465600N
Hema Atlas Map Ref 79 B6

1057

Milton Motor Camp

Taylor Park Recreation Reserve, Union St, Milton:
at north end of town, next to the swimming centre

Map 19 E5 A caretaker may collect fees if they are in attendance.

2274900E 5451400N
Hema Atlas Map Ref 79 C5

SH92 - Milton to Invercargill

1058

Roadside Rest Area

250m S of SH1 & SH8 intersection

Map 19 E5 Author's note - Sheltered with picnic tables.

2270700E 5448900N
Hema Atlas Map Ref 79 D5

1059

Naish Park Motor Camp

56 Charlotte St, Balclutha: signposted W of SH1
or Main St, Balclutha
Ph (03) 418 0088 naishparkmotorcamp@xtra.co.nz

Map 18 E4

2257600E 5436300N
Hema Atlas Map Ref 79 E3

1060 Kaka Point Camping Ground

Map 18 E4

39 Tarata St, Kaka Point: 14km from SH92, 7km S of
Balclutha; 10km from SH92, 7km N of Owaka
Ph/Fax (03) 412 8818

Author's note – Camping is not allowed on public reserves stretching sth
from Kaka Point to Nugget Point, but there are plenty of parking areas.

2261300E 5419900N
Hema Atlas Map Ref 79 G4

1061 Owaka Motor Camp

Map 18 E4

Ryley Street, Owaka: adjacent Catlins Inn
(03) 415 8350

2253500E 5413100N
Hema Atlas Map Ref 79 G3

1062 Keswick Park Family Camping Ground

Map 18 E4

2 Park Lane, Pounawea: off SH92 at Owaka
(03) 419 1110

2255100E 5409400N
Hema Atlas Map Ref 79 H3

1063 Pounawea Motor Camp

Map 18 E4

Park Lane, Pounawea: off SH92 at Owaka
Ph/Fax (03) 415 8483
pounawea.motor.camp@xtra.co.nz

2256400E 5409300N
Hema Atlas Map Ref 79 H3

1064 Catlins Woodstock Lodge & Camping Ground

Map 18 E4

Catlins Valley Rd: signposted W of main road,
approx 10km S of Owaka
Ph/Fax (03) 415 8583

Author's note – Laidback rural surrounds with nearby trout stream.

2246200E 5410900N
Hema Atlas Map Ref 79 G2

1065 Purakaunui Bay

Map 18 E4

Purakaunui Bay Scenic Reserve, Catlins Coast: E of SH92
DoC Coastal Otago Visitor Centre (03) 477 0677

2248900E 5401300N
Hema Atlas Map Ref 79 H2

1066 Tawanui

Map 18 E4

Catlins Conservation Park: W of Papatowai Hwy (SH92)
DoC Coastal Otago Visitor Centre (03) 477 0677

2239800E 5410200N
Hema Atlas Map Ref 79 G1

1067 Papatowai Motor Camp

Map 18 E4

2503 Papatowai Hwy (SH92): 26km S Owaka
DoC Coastal Otago Visitor Centre (03) 477 0677
or Bookings Ph/Fax (03) 415 8565

2239900E 5399400N
Hema Atlas Map Ref 79 J1

1068 Tautuku Beach Scenic Reserve

Map 18 E4

Adjacent SH92 (Southern Scenic Route): S of Papatowai

2238300E 5397200N
Hema Atlas Map Ref 79 J1

1069

Map 18 E4

Curio Bay Camping Ground

601 Waikawa-Curio Bay Rd, Curio Bay:
13km S SH92, via Waikawa
Ph (03) 246 8897

A caretaker may collect fees if they are in attendance. No pets allowed as penguins nest nearby. Author's note - Fossilised remains of a 160 million-year-old forest just a walk away.

2212000E 5387400N
Hema Atlas Map Ref 78 H11

1070

Map 18 E3

Fortrose Domain

SH92, Fortrose: 46km E of Invercargill

2188000E 5395000N
Hema Atlas Map Ref 78 G8

SH8 - Milton to Cromwell

1071

Map 18 E4

Tokamariro River Picnic Area

SH8: eastern end of Manuka Gorge, NW of Milton

Author's note - Sheltered spot with good trout fishing.

2266700E 5454600N
Hema Atlas Map Ref 79 C4

1072

Map 18 E4

Manuka Gorge Tunnel Rest Area

SH8: midway through Manuka Gorge, NW of Milton

2264900E 5455900N
Hema Atlas Map Ref 79 C4

1073

Map 18 D4

Lawrence Rest Area

SH8, Lawrence: E end of the town

2253400E 5470300N
Hema Atlas Map Ref 79 A3

1074

Map 18 D4

Gold Park Motor Camp

Harrington St, Lawrence: signposted at either end of Lawrence township
Ph (03) 485 9850

Author's note - Quiet, sheltered, rural location.

2252200E 5471000N
Hema Atlas Map Ref 79 A3

1075

Map 18 D4

Lawrence Rest Area

SH8, Lawrence: W end of the town

2251800E 5472500N
Hema Atlas Map Ref 79 A3

1076

Map 18 D4

Millers Flat Holiday Park

N of SH8 at Millers Flat: cross the Clutha River

A caretaker may collect fees if they are in attendance.

2230800E 5499800N
Hema Atlas Map Ref 73 F3

1077

Ettrick Holiday Park

7 James St, Ettrick

Ph (03) 446 6600

Map 18 D4   Author's note - Handy to seasonal fruit-picking work.

2226600E 5500600N

Hema Atlas Map Ref 73 E2

1078

Clutha River Rest Area

SH8: 2km E of Roxburgh, on the Clutha River

Map 18 D4   Author's note - Picnic spot with fishing potential.

2221300E 5508400N

Hema Atlas Map Ref 73 E2

1079

Roxburgh Rest Area

Adjacent SH8, Roxburgh: S end of town

Map 18 D4

2222300E 5511000N

Hema Atlas Map Ref 73 D2

1080

Gorge Creek Miners Monument & Picnic Area

SH8: about 25km N Roxburgh, 15km S Alexandra

Map 18 D4

2217800E 5530900N

Hema Atlas Map Ref 73 B1

1081

Butchers Dam Reserve

E of SH8: about 5km S Alexandra

Map 18 C4   Author's note - Fishing and swimming at the dam.

2224000E 5540100N

Hema Atlas Map Ref 73 B2

1082

Roadside Rest Area

SH8, Clyde: Otago Central Rail Trail start/finish

Map 18 C4

2222600E 5551300N

Hema Atlas Map Ref 66 J10

1083

Clyde Holiday & Sporting Complex

Whitby St, Clyde: signposted in Clyde township,
1km S of SH8

Ph (03) 449 2713 crrc@ihug.co.nz

Map 18 C4

2220700E 5551000N

Hema Atlas Map Ref 66 J10

1084

Clyde Dam Recreation Reserve

Just off SH8, Lake Dunstan: N end of Clyde

Map 18 C4   Author's note - Popular picnic and boating base.

2220200E 5553200N

Hema Atlas Map Ref 66 J10

1085

Champagne Creek Reserve

Adjacent SH8, Lake Dunstan: N of Clyde

Map 18 C4

2220900E 5558600N

Hema Atlas Map Ref 66 J10

1086

Map 18 C4

Nine Mile Creek Reserve

Adjacent SH8, Lake Dunstan: S of Cromwell

2216900E 5563000N
Hema Atlas Map Ref 66 H9

1087

Map 18 C4

Cromwell Top 10 Holiday Park

1 Alpha St, Cromwell: off SH8 at E end of Cromwell
Ph (03) 445 0164 or 0800 10 72 75
Info@cromwellholidaypark.co.nz
Author's note - Handy to Lake Dunstan for swimming and boating.

2211300E 5567000N
Hema Atlas Map Ref 66 H9

SH8 - Cromwell to Omarama (SH83)

1088

Map 18 C4

Roadside Rest Area

John Bulls Creek: W side of SH8 alongside Lake Dunstan

2213500E 5573000N
Hema Atlas Map Ref 66 G9

1089

Map 18 C4

Devils Creek Rest Area

Devils Creek: W side of SH8 alongside Lake Dunstan

2214100E 5574400N
Hema Atlas Map Ref 66 G9

1090

Map 18 C4

Bendigo Rest Area

Bendigo: W side of SH8 alongside Lake Dunstan

2216400E 5579300N
Hema Atlas Map Ref 66 G9

1091

Map 18 C4

Roadside Rest Area

Rocky Point: W side of SH8 alongside Lake Dunstan

2217500E 5580200N
Hema Atlas Map Ref 66 F9

1092

Map 18 C4

Roadside Rest Area

Bendigo: signposted E off SH8

Author's note - The 'ghost town' of Logantown and some
interesting old stone buildings, and mine shafts, are 3km up the hill
from this spot - take care.

2220600E 5581100N
Hema Atlas Map Ref 66 F10

1093

Map 18 C4

Roadside Rest Area

W side of SH8 in the Lindis Valley

Author's note - A favourite local swimming and fishing hole.

2232300E 5604300N
Hema Atlas Map Ref 66 D11

1094

Roadside Rest Area & Scenic Viewpoint

Alongside SH8, near the summit of Lindis Pass (967m)

Map 18 B4

2243400E 5620300N

Hema Atlas Map Ref 66 B12

1095

Roadside Rest Area

W side of SH8, beside the Dalrachney Bridge & Dalrachney Station entrance

Map 18 B4

2248900E 5627200N

Hema Atlas Map Ref 66 B12

1096

North Lindis Pass Rest Area

E side of SH8

Map 18 B4

2250700E 5626900N

Hema Atlas Map Ref 66 B13

1097

Roadside Rest Area

W side of SH8, 17km SW from Omarama

Map 18 B4   Entrance to the Ahuriri Conservation Park and Dingleburn Valley.

2252800E 5630200N

Hema Atlas Map Ref 66 A13

1098

Omarama Top 10 Holiday Park

1 Omarama Ave, Omarama

Ph (03) 438 9875 or 0800 662 726

omarama.holiday@xtra.co.nz

Map 19 B5

Author's note - Located in a ten acre park setting, and handy to world-class gliding facilities at Omarama Airport. There's also plentiful fishing in the nearby lakes and streams.

2268500E 5632400N

Hema Atlas Map Ref 67 A3

SH6 - Cromwell to Haast

1099

Chalets Holiday Park

102 Barry Ave, Cromwell: on road to Bannockburn, S of Cromwell

Ph (03) 445 1260 thechalets@xtra.co.nz

Map 18 C4   Author's note - Plenty of summer shade.

2210100E 5566100N

Hema Atlas Map Ref 66 H8

1100

Cairnmuir Lakeside Reserve

Cairnmuir Rd: E of Bannockburn Rd, just N of Bannockburn

Map 18 C4   Author's note - Ideal summer swimming and boating plus fishing.

2209700E 5563200N

Hema Atlas Map Ref 66 H8

1101

Cairnmuir Camping Ground

Cairnmuir Rd: E of Bannockburn Rd, just N of Bannockburn

Ph (03) 445 1956

Author's note - Surrounded by vineyards and adjoining a lake that's great for boating and swimming.

Map 18 C4

2209500E 5562000N

Hema Atlas Map Ref 66 H8

1102 Bannockburn Domain Motorcamp

Signposted just past the Hotel in Bannockburn township

Map 18 C4

A caretaker may collect fees if they are in attendance.

2207300E 5562600N
Hema Atlas Map Ref 66 H8

1103 Roadside Rest Area

E of SH6 on the SW edge of Lake Dunstan,
just N of Cromwell

Map 18 C4

2211600E 5569200N
Hema Atlas Map Ref 66 H9

1104 Lowburn Rest Area

Lowburn: E of SH6

Map 18 C4

2212100E 5570500N
Hema Atlas Map Ref 66 G9

1105 Luggate Domain

W side of SH6, 800m N of Luggate

Map 18 C4

A caretaker may collect fees or donations. Author's note - Sheltered and handy to Wanaka, with cheap rates.

2213300E 5600600N
Hema Atlas Map Ref 66 D9

1106 Wanaka Lakeview Holiday Park

212 Brownston St, Wanaka: signposted from the Lakeside,
W of Wanaka township, W of Pembrook Park
Ph (03) 443 7883 martin_@xtra.co.nz

Map 18 C4

Author's note - The facilities are a bit dated and it's rather crowded in the peak Dec/Jan period, however the almost waterfront location close to the town centre more than compensates.

2203900E 5604100N
Hema Atlas Map Ref 66 D8

1107 Roadside Rest Area

Beacon Point Reserve, Beacon Point Rd, Lake Wanaka

Map 18 C4

2202200E 5607000N
Hema Atlas Map Ref 66 D8

1108 Lake Outlet Motor Camp

Lake Outlet, Wanaka: signposted from SH6 intersection with Anderson Rd on the E edge of Wanaka township, and also from Aubrey Rd
Ph (03) 443 7478

Map 18 C4

Author's note - Simple camping adjoining the lake, and it's a favoured fishing area.

2204600E 5608100N
Hema Atlas Map Ref 66 D8

1109 Roadside Rest Area

N side of the Mt Aspiring Rd at Roys Bay, Lake Wanaka

Map 18 C4

2203000E 5605300N
Hema Atlas Map Ref 66 D8

1110

Map 18 C4

Top 10 Pleasant Point Lodge Holiday Park

217 Mt Aspiring Rd, Wanaka: W of Wanaka township
Ph (03) 443 7360 plelow@xtra.co.nz

Author's note - Qualmark four star facilities.

2201400E 5605200N
Hema Atlas Map Ref 66 D8

1111

Map 18 C4

Aspiring Caravan Park

Studholme Rd, Wanaka: signposted S off the
Mt Aspiring Rd, W of Wanaka township
Ph (03) 443 6603 or 0800 229 8439
info@caravanpark.co.nz

Author's note - This park has modern facilities, but is more
suitable for mobile campervans than tents.

2201700E 5603800N
Hema Atlas Map Ref 66 D8

1112

Map 18 C3

Glendhu Bay Motor Camp

Lakeside at Glendhu Bay: 11km from Wanaka
on the Mt Aspiring Rd
Ph (03) 443 7243 glendhucamp@xtra.co.nz

Author's note - An iconic family-friendly lakeside holiday park.
It's very popular so has a tendancy to be crowded throughout the
Christmas/New Year/January period.

2194400E 5607800N
Hema Atlas Map Ref 65 D7

1113

Map 18 C4

Albert Town Reserve

Adjacent SH6: 5km NE of Wanaka, N bank of the
Clutha River at the Albert Town bridge
DoC Mt Aspiring NP Visitor Centre Ph (03) 443 7660
wanakavc@doc.govt.nz

Author's note - Riverside in a prime trout-fishing spot, and only five
minutes from the centre of Wanaka.

2207500E 5608300N
Hema Atlas Map Ref 66 D8

1114

Map 18 C4

Lake Hawea Holiday Park

SW corner of Lake Hawea, off SH6
Ph (03) 443 1767

Author's note - During the less crowded, off-peak times this camp
is an understated gem. Lakeside swimming, fishing and boating
opportunities abound.

2212700E 5616200N
Hema Atlas Map Ref 66 C9

1115

Map 18 B4

Lake Hawea Lookout

Adjacent Lake Hawea & SH6, about halfway along the Lake

2212400E 5626700N
Hema Atlas Map Ref 66 B9

1116

Map 18 B4

Roadside Rest Area

The 'Neck': 32km from Wanaka on Lake Hawea

2207800E 5634800N
Hema Atlas Map Ref 66 A8

1117 — Kidds Bush Reserve

Map 18 B4

6km off SH6, at the 'Neck': between Lakes Hawea and Wanaka, 32km from Wanaka
DoC Mt Aspiring Visitor Information Centre
Ph (03) 443 7660 wanakavc@doc.govt.nz
Author's note - A pretty, sheltered and remote spot that's a favoured trout-fishing base.

2212400E 5633500N
Hema Atlas Map Ref 66 A9

1118 — Boundary Creek

Map 18 B4

Off SH6, head of Lake Wanaka: 32km from Wanaka & SE of Makarora
DoC Makarora Visitor Centre Ph (03) 443 8365
makaroavc@doc.govt.nz
Author's note - A sheltered lakeside campsite in a pretty location.

2207300E 5643900N
Hema Atlas Map Ref 58 J10

1119 — Makarora Wilderness Resort

Map 18 B4

5955 Hawea Rd, Makarora
Ph (03) 443 8372 info@makarora.co.nz
Author's note - A pleasant base from which to explore this alpine area. Jet boats and planes can be hired to transport you to remote areas.

2209800E 5656600N
Hema Atlas Map Ref 58 H11

1120 — Blue Pools Roadside Rest Area

Map 18 B4

SH6: NW of Makarora
DoC Makarora Visitor Centre Ph (03) 443 8365
makaroavc@doc.govt.nz

2211500E 5665200N
Hema Atlas Map Ref 58 G11

1121 — Cameron Flat, Mount Aspiring National Park

Map 18 B4

SH6: 8km NW of Makarora
DoC Makarora Visitor Centre Ph (03) 443 8365
makaroavc@doc.govt.nz

2212700E 5665800N
Hema Atlas Map Ref 58 G11

1122 — Cameron Creek Rest Area

Map 18 B4

SH6: SE of Haast Summit

2213800E 5666900N
Hema Atlas Map Ref 58 G11

1123 — Davis Flat Roadside Rest Area

Map 18 B4

SH6: SE of Haast Summit

2217600E 5668200N
Hema Atlas Map Ref 58 G11

1124 — Fantail Falls Roadside Rest Area

Map 18 B4

SH6: SE of Gates of Haast

2221300E 5674400N
Hema Atlas Map Ref 58 F12

1125 Gates of Haast Bridge

SH6: Gates of Haast

Map 18 B4

2220700E 5679500N
Hema Atlas Map Ref 58 F12

1126 Thunder Creek Falls & Forest Walk

SH6: 2km W of Gates of Haast

Map 18 B4

2219500E 5680000N
Hema Atlas Map Ref 58 F11

1127 Pleasant Flat

SH6, Pleasant Flat: 45km E of Haast
DoC Haast Visitor Centre Ph (03) 750 0809
haastvc@doc.govt.nz

Map 18 B4

2222100E 5682000N
Hema Atlas Map Ref 58 E12

1128 Clarkes Bluff

SH6: at the confluence of the Landsborough & Haast rivers

Map 18 B4

2223700E 5686300N
Hema Atlas Map Ref 58 E12

1129 Roaring Billy Falls Reserve

SH6: SE of Haast

Map 18 B4

2211800E 5690500N
Hema Atlas Map Ref 58 D11

SH6 & SH6A - Cromwell to Glenorchy

1130 Roaring Meg Viewpoint and Picnic Area

Adjacent SH6 and Kawarau River

The picnic area is on the opposite side of the road, so take care with the traffic. Author's note - If you are lucky you may see canoeists shooting the rapids here.

Map 18 C4

2200500E 5570300N
Hema Atlas Map Ref 66 G8

1131 Arrowtown Holiday Park

11 Suffolk St, Arrowtown: signposted from E of town centre
Ph/Fax (03) 442 1876 arrowtownholidaypark@xtra.co.nz

Author's note - Handy to the public swimming pool and tennis courts, and only 200m from the town centre.

Map 18 C3

2181400E 5576400N
Hema Atlas Map Ref 65 G6

1132 Macetown

15km up the Arrow River from Arrowtown
(4WD only with river crossings)
DoC Queenstown Visitor Centre Ph (03) 442 7935
queenstownvc@doc.govt.na

Stream water only

Map 18 C3

2180600E 5586800N
Hema Atlas Map Ref 65 F6

1133

Map 18 C3

Frankton Motor Camp
Yewlett Crescent, Frankton, Queenstown: signposted one block from Frankton roundabout
Ph (03) 442 2079
Author's note - Lakeside for fishing, swimming and boating

2173100E 5567500N
Hema Atlas Map Ref 126 A5, 65 H5

1134

Map 18 C3

Kawarau Falls Lakeside Holiday Park
SH6, Queenstown: just across the Kawarau River, S of Frankton
Ph 0800 226 774 relax@campsite.co.nz
Author's note - Lakeside for fishing, swimming & boating.

2174000E 5566300N
Hema Atlas Map Ref 126 B6, 65 H5

1135

Map 18 C3

Queenstown Lake View Holiday Park
Brecon St, Queenstown: follow signs to Gondola terminal from Queenstown town centre
Ph (03) 442 7252 or 0800 482 7352
holidaypark@qldc.govt.nz
Author's note - Brand new, architect-designed facilities, only 150m from town centre.

2168200E 5567300N
Hema Atlas Ref 125 B2, 126 B2, 65 H4

1136

Map 18 C3

Queenstown Rest Area
Follow signs from Queenstown centre towards Glenorchy

2167300E 5565800N
Hema Atlas Ref 125 D1, 126 B2, 65 H4

1137

Map 18 C3

Queenstown Top 10 Holiday Park
54 Robins Rd, Queenstown: signposted from roundabout near recreation reserve and fire station
Ph (03) 442 9447 or 0800 786 222 creekside@camp.co.nz
Author's note - This environmentally certified park is 'clean and green', and handy to the town centre.

2168200E 5567300N
Hema Atlas Ref 125 A2, 126 B2, 65 H4

1138

Map 18 C3

Shotover Top 10 Holiday Park
70 Arthurs Point Rd, Queenstown: adjacent the Queenstown to Arrowtown Rd, N of Arthurs Point, 1.5km S of the Coronet Peak Skifield turnoff. Ph (03) 442 9306 or 0800 462 267 stay@shotoverholidaypark.co.nz
Author's note - Handy to the Coronet Peak and Shotover Jet attractions.

2168600E 5572300N
Hema Atlas Map Ref 65 G4

1139
Map 18 C3

Skippers-Mt Aurum
Skippers Rd: 26km from Queenstown
DoC Queenstown Visitor Centre Ph (03) 442 7935
queenstownvc@doc.govt.na

2168400E 5585400N
Hema Atlas Map Ref 65 F4

1140
Map 18 C3

Moke Lake
Glenorchy Rd: about 12km W of Queenstown
DoC Queenstown Visitor Centre Ph (03) 442 7935
queenstownvc@doc.govt.na
Stream water only.
Author's note - A world away from Queenstown, yet so close.

2160600E 5567700N
Hema Atlas Map Ref 65 H4

1141 Map 18 C3

Twelve Mile Delta
Glenorchy Rd: 11km from Queenstown,
signposted on road to Glenorchy
DoC Queenstown Visitor Centre Ph (03) 442 7935
queenstownvc@doc.govt.na
Stream water only

2158900E 5562700N
Hema Atlas Map Ref 65 H3

1142 Map 18 C3

Glenorchy Lakeside Reserve
Glenorchy Rd, Glenorchy

2144800E 5584600N
Hema Atlas Map Ref 65 F2

1143 Map 18 C3

Glenorchy Holiday Park
Oban St, Glenorchy
Ph (03) 442 9943 www.glenorchyinfocentre.co.nz
Author's note - Lakeside, and handy to the town centre.

2146400E 5585200N
Hema Atlas Map Ref 65 F2

1144 Map 18 C3

Kinloch
Kinloch Rd: 24km from Glenorchy
DoC Queenstown Visitor Centre Ph (03) 442 7935
queenstownvc@doc.govt.na
Stream water only Author's note - Lakeside for fishing and swimming

2143200E 5585500N
Hema Atlas Map Ref 65 F2

1145 Map 18 C3

Lake Sylvan
Routeburn Rd, beside Routeburn River:
20km from Glenorchy
DoC Queenstown Visitor Centre Ph (03) 442 7935
queenstownvc@doc.govt.na
Author's note - Nice walking nearby.

2139000E 5598900N
Hema Atlas Map Ref 65 E1

FIORDLAND & SOUTHLAND REGION

Lake Te Anau

SH6 - Queenstown to Invercargill

1146 Map 18 D3

Lakeside Rest Area
SH6: S end of Lake Wakatipu

Author's note - Sheltered with picnic tables.

2177100E 5538000N
Hema Atlas Map Ref 72 B8

1147

Map 18 D3

Kingston Flyer Northern Railway Terminal & Reserve

W of SH6 at Kingston

2173800E 5533700N
Hema Atlas Map Ref 72 B8

1148

Map 18 D3

Kingston Motels & Holiday Park

Kent St, Kingston
Ph/Fax (03) 248 8501 peterm@xtra.co.nz

Author's note - Fishing and walking nearby, as well as the Kingston Flyer for steamtrain enthusiasts.

2175000E 5533400N
Hema Atlas Map Ref 72 B8

1149

Map 18 D3

Kingston Flyer Southern Railway Terminal & Reserve

SH6, S of Kingston

2171700E 5522000N
Hema Atlas Map Ref 72 C8

1150

Map 18 D3

Glenquoich Caravan Park

Albion Street, Athol
Ph (03) 248 8987

2164000E 5513900N
Hema Atlas Map Ref 71 D7

1151

Map 18 D3

Mossburn Country Park

Mossburn Five Rivers Rd, Mossburn: just N of Mossburn
Ph (03) 248 6313 paddypam@xtra.co.nz

Author's note - Under new management, with a welcoming manner.

2140900E 5496100N
Hema Atlas Map Ref 71 F5

1152

Map 18 D4

Piano Flat

23km N of Waikaia: off SH94 at Riversdale
DoC Fiordland National Park Visitor Centre
Ph (03) 249 7924 fiordlandvc@doc.govt.nz

Fees usually via self registration envelopes

2199900E 5508600N
Hema Atlas Map Ref 72 E11

1153

Map 18 E3

Dolamore Park

No. 7 RD, Gore: off SH94
Ph (03) 208 6896

2187500E 5453000N
Hema Atlas Map Ref 78 A8

1154

Map 18 E3

Gore Motor Camp

35 Broughton St, Gore: W of SH1, S of town centre
Ph/Fax (03) 208 4919 gorecamp@xtra.co.nz

Author's note - A little known gem that's well signposted.

2195200E 5448100N
Hema Atlas Map Ref 78 B9

1155

Map 18 E3

Winton Golf Course & Camp

Sub Station Road, Winton
(03) 236 8422

2146900E 5440600N
Hema Atlas Map Ref 77 B4

1156 — Invercargill Top 10 Holiday Park

Map 18 E3

77 McIvor Rd, Invercargill: E of SH6, 6km from Invercargill
Ph (03) 215 9032 or 0800 486 873
gumtreefarmmp@xtra.co.nz

2153700E 5417700N
Hema Atlas Map Ref 77 E5

1157 — Lorneville Holiday Park

Map 18 E3

352 Lorneville-Dacre Rd, Invercargill:
E of SH6, 8km N of Invercargill, on SH98
Ph (03) 235 8031 lornepark@xtra.co.nz

2155400E 5418100N
Hema Atlas Map Ref 77 E5

1158 — Invercargill Caravan Park

Map 18 E3

20 Victoria Ave, Invercargill: signposted S of Dee St
Ph/Fax (03) 218 8787

Author's note - The handiest park to the city centre.

2151300E 5412900N
Hema Atlas Ref 127 A1, 128 C3, 77 E5

1159 — Amble on Inn Holiday Park

Map 18 E3

145 Chesney St, Invercargill: signposted E
of Invercargill, enroute to Catlins
Ph (03) 216 5214 ambleoninn@xtra.co.nz

2155400E 5409300N
Hema Atlas Map Ref 128 B5, 77 F5

1160 — Argyle Park Motorcamp

Map 18 E3

Gregory St, Bluff: signposted S end of town, off Marine Pde
Ph (03) 212 8704

2153600E 5389900N
Hema Atlas Map Ref 77 G5

1161 — Otatara Beach Rd Motor Camp

Map 18 E3

375 Dunns Road, Otatara
Ph (03) 213 0400

2145400E 5408100N
Hema Atlas Map Ref 77 F4

SH99 - Invercargill to Te Anau

1162 — Longwood Lodge Caravan Park

Map 18 E3

43 Richard St, Riverton: follow signs S on W side of bridge
Ph/Fax (03) 234 8132

2125400E 5415700N
Hema Atlas Map Ref 76 H14

1163 — Riverton Caravan Park

Map 18 E3

Hamlet St, Riverton: follow signs S on W side of bridge
Ph/Fax (03) 234 8526

2126400E 5414500N
Hema Atlas Map Ref 76 H14

1164

Map 18 E3

Riverton Rocks Scenic Reserve

The Rocks: SE of Riverton

2127700E 5413500N
Hema Atlas Map Ref 77 E2

1165

Map 18 E2

Camp Oraka

Colac Bay: 11km W Riverton

2115200E 5414600N
Hema Atlas Map Ref 76 H13

1166

Map 18 E2

Tuatapere Motel, Backpacker & Holiday Park

73 Main St, Tuatapere
Ph (03) 226 6250
shooters.backpackers@xtra.co.nz

2100500E 5438900N
Hema Atlas Map Ref 76 F12

1167

Map 18 E2

Five Mountains Holiday Park

6 Clifden Rd, Tuatapere: E of SH99 at N end of town
Ph (03) 226 6418

2098400E 5440100N
Hema Atlas Map Ref 76 E11

1168

Map 18 E2

Tuatapere Domain Reserve

Riverside spot off Elder Drive, Tuatapere
Ph (03) 226 6650

2099500E 5441100N
Hema Atlas Map Ref 76 E11

1169

Map 18 E2

Clifden Suspension Bridge Reserve

14km N of Tuatapere on SH99

Author's note - Riverside spot suited to fishing and swimming.

2100400E 5451800N
Hema Atlas Map Ref 76 D12

1170

Map 18 E2

Thicket Burn

Lake Hauroko Rd: 25km W of Clifden
DoC Fiordland National Park Visitor Centre
Ph (03) 249 7924 fiordlandvc@doc.govt.nz
Fees usually via self registration envelopes

2080300E 5451500N
Hema Atlas Map Ref 76 D10

1171

Map 18 E2

Lake Hauroko

Lake Hauroko road end: 32km W of Clifden
DoC Fiordland National Park Visitor Centre
Ph (03) 249 7924 fiordlandvc@doc.govt.nz
Stream water only; fees usually via self registration envelopes

2075500E 5454500N
Hema Atlas Map Ref 76 D9

1172

Map 18 D2

Monowai

Lake Monowai road end
DoC Fiordland National Park Visitor Centre
Ph (03) 249 7924 fiordlandvc@doc.govt.nz
Fees usually via self registration envelopes

2083600E 5474000N
Hema Atlas Map Ref 76 B10

1173 **Manapouri Lakeside Reserve**

Waterfront at Manapouri township

2088900E 5502400N

Author's note - Swimming, fishing and boating options.

Hema Atlas Map Ref 70 E10

Map 18 D2

1174 **Lakeview Chalets & Motor Camp**

50 Manapouri Te Anau Rd, Manapouri: across the road from the lake, N end of Manapouri
Ph (03) 249 6624 manapouri@xtra.co.nz

Author's note - Charming in a budget way.

2089600E 5503500N

Map 18 D2

Hema Atlas Map Ref 70 E10

SH94 - Te Anau to Milford Sound

1175 **Te Anau Lake View Holiday Park**

Te Anau-Manapouri Rd, Te Anau
Ph (03) 249 7457 res@teanau.info

Author's note - Lakeside and walk to the town centre

2095700E 5518600N

Map 18 D2

Hema Atlas Map Ref 70 D11

1176 **Te Anau Top 10 Holiday Park**

128 Te Anau Tce, Te Anau: 200m W of town centre
Ph 0800 249 746 fivestar@teanautop10.co.nz

Author's note - Everything you need in a compact, sheltered environment.

2095700E 5518600N

Map 18 D2

Hema Atlas Map Ref 70 D11

1177 **Great Lakes Holiday Park**

Cnr Luxmore & Milford Rd, Te Anau: W of Caltex Station
Ph 0800 249 555 teanaugreatlakesholidaypark@xtra.co.nz

2096200E 5519800N

Map 18 D2

Hema Atlas Map Ref 70 D11

1178 **Mavora Lakes**

Off SH94: about 40km N of SH94
DoC Fiordland National Park Visitor Centre
Ph (03) 249 7924 fiordlandvc@doc.govt.nz

Stream water only; fees usually via self registration envelopes

2130900E 5536200N

Map 18 D3

Hema Atlas Map Ref 71 B4

1179 **Fiordland Great Views Holiday Park**

Milford Rd, Te Anau: 1.5km N of Te Anau
Ph (03) 249 7059 fiordland.holiday.park@xtra.co.nz

Author's note - Spacious, sheltered and quiet - it's a place to escape Te Anau when it gets hectic.

2098200E 5520900N

Map 18 D2

Hema Atlas Map Ref 70 C11

1180 **Henry Creek**

Adjacent SH94 (Milford Rd): 25km N Te Anau
DoC Fiordland National Park Visitor Centre
Ph (03) 249 7924 fiordlandvc@doc.govt.nz

Stream water only; fires not permitted

2102100E 5540000N

Map 18 C2

Hema Atlas Map Ref 70 B12

1181

Te Anau Downs

Adjacent SH94 (Milford Rd): 33km N Te Anau
Ph 0800 500 706 grumpys@xtra.co.nz

Map 18 C2

Only 600m from the Milford Track Great Walk departure point

2102700E 5543900N
Hema Atlas Map Ref 70 A12

1182

Te Anau Downs Rest Area

Adjacent SH94 (Milford Rd): N Te Anau

Map 18 C2

2103300E 5545100N
Hema Atlas Map Ref 70 A12

1183

Walker Creek

Adjacent SH94 (Milford Rd): 49km N Te Anau
DoC Fiordland National Park Visitor Centre
Ph (03) 249 7924 fiordlandvc@doc.govt.nz

Map 18 C2

Stream water only; fees usually via self registration envelopes

2113500E 5556000N
Hema Atlas Map Ref 64 J9

1184

Totara

Adjacent SH94 (Milford Rd): 53km N Te Anau
DoC Fiordland National Park Visitor Centre
Ph (03) 249 7924 fiordlandvc@doc.govt.nz

Map 18 C2

Stream water only; fees usually via self registration envelopes

2116200E 5557900N
Hema Atlas Map Ref 64 J9

1185

McKay Creek

Adjacent SH94 (Milford Rd): 53km N Te Anau
DoC Fiordland National Park Visitor Centre
Ph (03) 249 7924 fiordlandvc@doc.govt.nz

Map 18 C2

Stream water only; fees usually via self registration envelopes

2114900E 5559300N
Hema Atlas Map Ref 64 J9

1186

Mirror Lakes DoC Reserve

Adjacent SH94 (Milford Rd): N Te Anau

Map 18 C2

Author's note - Well worth the walk to view the mirror reflections of adjacent mountains (providing there is no wind).

2116000E 5563800N
Hema Atlas Map Ref 64 H9

1187

Deer Flat

Adjacent SH94 (Milford Rd): 62km N Te Anau
DoC Fiordland National Park Visitor Centre
Ph (03) 249 7924 fiordlandvc@doc.govt.nz

Map 18 C2

Stream water only; fees usually via self registration envelopes

2116200E 5567300N
Hema Atlas Map Ref 64 H9

1188

Knobs Flat Rest Area

Adjacent SH94 (Milford Rd), Knobs Flat: 65km N Te Anau

Map 18 C2

Author's note - Pretty much just a toilet stop for all the tourist buses that ply this route.

2117900E 5568700N
Hema Atlas Map Ref 64 H9

1189

Kiosk Creek

Adjacent SH94 (Milford Rd): 65km N Te Anau
DoC Fiordland National Park Visitor Centre
Ph (03) 249 7924 fiordlandvc@doc.govt.nz

Map 18 C2

Stream water only; fees usually via self registration envelopes

2119100E 5568700N
Hema Atlas Map Ref 64 H9

1190 Smithy Creek

Map 18 C2

Adjacent SH94 (Milford Rd): 67km N Te Anau
DoC Fiordland National Park Visitor Centre
Ph (03) 249 7924 fiordlandvc@doc.govt.nz
Stream water only; fees usually via self registration envelopes

2117900E 5572600N
Hema Atlas Map Ref 64 G9

1191 Upper Eglinton

Map 18 C2

Adjacent SH94 (Milford Rd): 71km N Te Anau
DoC Fiordland National Park Visitor Centre
Ph (03) 249 7924 fiordlandvc@doc.govt.nz
Stream water only; fees usually via self registration envelopes

2116800E 5575000N
Hema Atlas Map Ref 64 G9

1192 Cascade Creek

Map 18 C2

Adjacent SH94 (Milford Rd): 76km N Te Anau
DoC Fiordland National Park Visitor Centre
Ph (03) 249 7924 fiordlandvc@doc.govt.nz
Stream water only: fees usually via self registration envelopes

2121100E 5579300N
Hema Atlas Map Ref 64 G10

1193 Lake Gunn

Map 18 C2

Adjacent SH94 (Milford Rd): 78km N Te Anau
DoC Fiordland National Park Visitor Centre
Ph (03) 249 7924 fiordlandvc@doc.govt.nz
Stream water only; fees usually via self registration envelopes

2122200E 5583500N
Hema Atlas Map Ref 64 F10

1194 The Divide & Routeburn Track Base

Map 18 C3

Adjacent SH94 (Milford Rd): 89km N Te Anau

2124700E 5586200N
Hema Atlas Map Ref 64 F10

1195 The Chasm

Map 18 C2

Adjacent SH94 (Milford Rd): half way between the Homer
Tunnel and Milford Sound

Author's note - Spectacular viewing to appreciate just how water can
wear rock in a climate like this.

2109300E 5597500N
Hema Atlas Map Ref 64 E8

1196 Milford Sound Lodge

Map 18 C2

Milford Sound: on the S edge of Milford Sound township
Ph (03) 249 8071 info@milfordlodge.com

2109700E 5603100N
Hema Atlas Map Ref 64 D8